ALGEBRA 1
ANSWER KEY & TEST BANK

Table of Contents

Problem Set Answers — 1

Chapter Tests — 57

Chapter Test Answers — 125

Algebra 1: A Teaching Textbook™
2.0 Version
Answer Key and Test Bank
Greg Sabouri and Shawn Sabouri

Printed in the United States of America.

ISBN: 978-0-9835812-1-5

Teaching Textbooks, Inc.
P. O. Box 16310
Oklahoma City, OK 73113
www.teachingtextbooks.com

PROBLEM SET ANSWERS

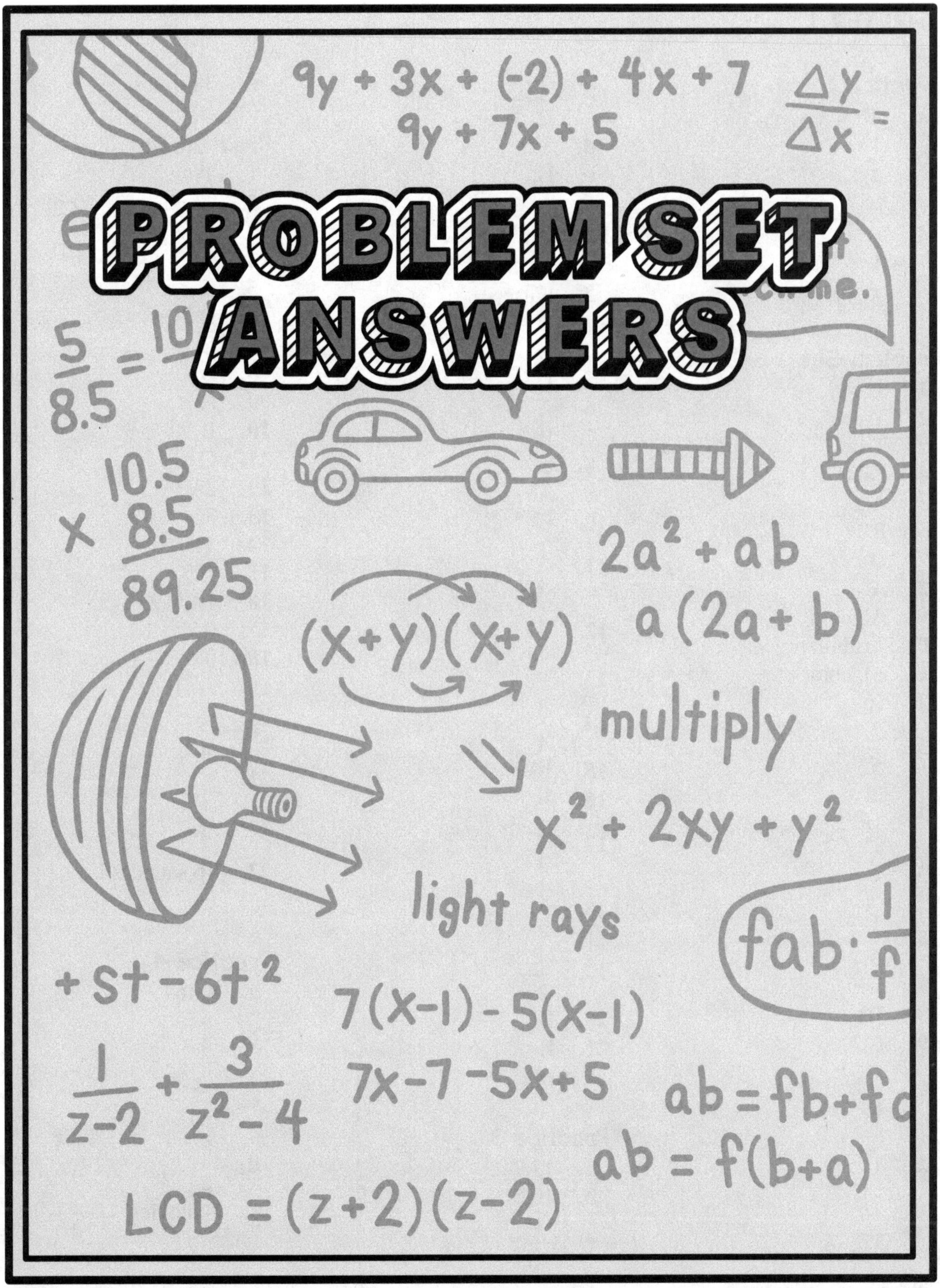

CHAPTER 1

Practice 1

a. 30
b. $\frac{1}{4}$
c. 7
d. 1
e. $\frac{1}{5}$

Problem Set 1

1. True
2. True
3. True
4. False
5. A
6. B
7. D
8. A
9. Algebra
10. Arithmetic
11. Algebra
12. 56
13. $\frac{3}{5}$
14. $\frac{2}{15}$
15. $\frac{3}{4}$
16. $\frac{1}{6}$
17. 3
18. 3.2
19. 1
20. $\frac{1}{8}$
21. 1
22. 0

Practice 2

a. D
b. $\frac{5}{6}$
c. $\frac{1}{2}$
d. Yes
e. E

Problem Set 2

1. True
2. False
3. D
4. E
5. D
6. A
7. B
8. C
9. A
10. E
11. $\frac{1}{9}$
12. $\frac{5}{8}$
13. 3
14. $\frac{3}{4}$
15. 10
16. 7
17. $\frac{2}{3}$
18. $\frac{5}{9}$
19. $\frac{2}{27}$
20. E
21. E

Practice 3

a. 12,742
b. 10.5
c. $\frac{1}{16}$
d. $\frac{1}{2}$
e. 38 times

Problem Set 3

1. True
2. True
3. True
4. A
5. E
6. D
7. D
8. B
9. E
10. B
11. C
12. 38
13. 36
14. 11
15. 123
16. 10,519
17. 0
18. 0.6
19. 14.4
20. $\frac{1}{4}$
21. 1
22. $\frac{1}{2}$
23. 16 sandcastles

Practice 4

a. 1,464
b. $\frac{4}{3}$
c. $\frac{3}{10}$
d. $\frac{8}{5}$
e. 8 movies

Problem Set 4

1. False
2. False
3. True.
4. A
5. B
6. E
7. D
8. A
9. B
10. C
11. 382
12. 187
13. 5,702
14. 3
15. 8,346
16. 3.02
17. 62.1
18. $\frac{3}{20}$
19. $\frac{33}{10}$
20. $\frac{7}{16}$
21. $\frac{11}{21}$
22. 246 appearances

Practice 5

a. Yes
b. No
c. $\frac{1}{12}$
d. $\frac{5}{2}$
e. 504 parasites

Problem Set 5

1. True
2. True
3. True
4. True
5. C
6. A
7. B
8. E
9. C
10. Yes
11. No
12. Yes
13. No
14. 36
15. 16.8
16. 1
17. $\frac{2}{15}$
18. $\frac{11}{20}$
19. 29.24
20. $\frac{3}{2}$
21. $\frac{8}{5}$
22. $\frac{2}{9}$
23. 2,282 faults

Practice 6

a. C
b. A
c. $\frac{1}{5}$
d. $\frac{3}{8}$
e. 22 carrots each day

Problem Set 6

1. True
2. False
3. True
4. E
5. B
6. D
7. B
8. E
9. D
10. Yes
11. Yes
12. No
13. $\frac{1}{8}$
14. $\frac{17}{2}$
15. $\frac{2}{11}$
16. $\frac{1}{9}$
17. 49.14
18. $\frac{5}{6}$
19. 16
20. 6.5
21. 6.6
22. 20 months

Practice 7

a. $\frac{9}{100}$
b. 0.03
c. 0.062
d. $\frac{1}{5}$
e. 28,000 people

Problem Set 7

1. True
2. False
3. False
4. True
5. E
6. D
7. C
8. D
9. $\frac{7}{100}$
10. 0.04

11. 0.025
12. Yes
13. Yes
14. 19
15. 18
16. 51
17. 2,000
18. 8
19. 5,000
20. 1
21. $\frac{1}{3}$
22. 25,500 people

Practice 8

a. 83%
b. $\frac{51}{1,000}$
c. $\frac{2}{3}$
d. 200
e. $20,000

Problem Set 8

1. True
2. True
3. True
4. 0.325
5. 91%
6. $\frac{73}{1,000}$
7. D
8. A
9. Yes
10. No
11. No
12. $\frac{1}{10}$
13. 132
14. 42
15. $\frac{31}{12}$
16. 7.7
17. 3.75
18. $\frac{2}{5}$
19. $\frac{7}{8}$
20. 250
21. $50,000

Practice 9

a. 12%
b. 40 miles
c. 1,400 millimeters
d. 1.2 yards
e. 3.8 hours

Problem Set 9

1. True
2. True
3. True
4. 0.0015
5. 18%
6. 120 miles
7. 58.8 feet
8. 2,500 millimeters
9. 4.3 yards
10. 3 days
11. Yes
12. No
13. $\frac{13}{4}$
14. 5.7
15. 12
16. 13
17. $\frac{1}{8}$
18. $\frac{7}{9}$
19. 28
20. $\frac{1}{2}$
21. $\frac{11}{32}$
22. 645.3 hours

Practice 10

a. $3x$ people
b. 6 days
c. 0.2 or $\frac{1}{5}$
d. $\frac{1}{3}$
e. 7,533 miles

Problem Set 10

1. True
2. True
3. 20 people
4. $5x$ people
5. 240 minutes
6. 18 days
7. 300 seconds
8. 14 miles
9. Yes
10. Yes
11. No
12. $\frac{1}{2}$ or 0.5
13. $\frac{4}{3}$
14. $\frac{1}{4}$
15. 10
16. 1
17. $\frac{1}{6}$
18. 3
19. $\frac{3}{8}$
20. 0.21
21. 2,548 cups

CHAPTER 2

Practice 11

a. 6, 1, 0, $-3, -3.5, -6$

b. 16, -11, 3.2, -56, $-\frac{3}{4}$

c. Yes

d. $\frac{1}{6}$

e. 47 cents

Problem Set 11

1. True
2. True
3. False
4. B
5. A
6. -1
7. 

8. $-12, -12.2, -55, -55.5$
9. $4, -7, 2.5, -101, -\frac{1}{2}$
10. Yes
11. Yes
12. No
13. -8
14. $\frac{1}{9}$
15. -6
16. $\frac{5}{9}$
17. $\frac{1}{22}$
18. 67
19. $\frac{19}{20}$
20. 5.1
21. 15
22. 32 cents

Practice 12

a. $-1{,}500$

b. No

c. $3x$ fences

d. $\frac{11}{12}$

e. 23 days

Problem Set 12

1. True
2. True
3. False
4. True
5. -2
6. -8
7. -14
8. -100
9. No
10. Yes
11. 12 times
12. $2x$ damsels
13. 3,000
14. $\frac{17}{3}$
15. $\frac{10}{7}$
16. -10
17. -12
18. 96
19. 11
20. 2.5
21. $\frac{9}{14}$
22. 28 days

Practice 13

a. 13

b. $-\frac{5}{8}$

c. -18

d. 6

e. 420 dolphins

Problem Set 13

1. C
2. C
3. B
4. 5
5. $-\frac{19}{28}$
6. 9
7. -5
8. 20
9. $-\frac{1}{3}$
10. -8.1
11. $-\frac{5}{8}$
12. $-\frac{13}{6}$
13. 450 miles
14. $4y$ apples
15. $\frac{3}{10}$
16. -30
17. $\frac{7}{3}$
18. 33
19. 1,176
20. -47
21. 20 bars

Practice 14

a. -20

b. 11

c. $\frac{7}{8}$

d. No

e. 160 people

Problem Set 14

1. A
2. B
3. B
4. 3

5. -14
6. -1
7. -18
8. 46
9. -14.1
10. $\frac{5}{4}$
11. $-18{,}000$
12. 0
13. 0.25 or $\frac{1}{4}$ minutes
14. $11x$ dollars
15. Yes
16. No
17. 0.08
18. 3
19. -14
20. $\frac{1}{5}$
21. 8.47
22. 115,703,826 jelly beans

Practice 15

a. -45
b. $\frac{4}{5}$
c. 0
d. Yes
e. 8.5%

Problem Set 15

1. B
2. A
3. A
4. B
5. -5
6. 46
7. 3
8. 17.7
9. -4
10. $\frac{1}{2}$
11. -60
12. -2
13. 64
14. $\frac{7}{12}$
15. -3
16. 0
17. Yes
18. Yes
19. $\frac{2}{3}$
20. 100
21. 0
22. 9.5%

Practice 16

a. -3.2
b. 8.6
c. -9
d. $\frac{1}{2}$
e. 20,500 pounds

Problem Set 16

1. A
2. B
3. A
4. B
5. 0
6. -39
7. -3.9
8. $-\frac{4}{7}$
9. $\frac{11}{18}$
10. -27.1
11. -42
12. $-\frac{1}{4}$
13. 15.4
14. -5
15. -23
16. 5
17. $\frac{2}{3}$
18. -3
19. $-\frac{1}{3}$
20. 91
21. 18
22. $\frac{5}{9}$
23. 0.02 grams

Practice 17

a. Yes
b. Yes
c. -9
d. 8
e. -35 degrees

Problem Set 17

1. -7
2. $-\frac{19}{24}$
3. -3.7
4. 12
5. 7
6. -3
7. 1
8. 0
9. -10
10. Yes
11. Yes
12. Yes
13. Yes
14. 18
15. 132
16. -123
17. -20
18. -15
19. -306
20. -4
21. -58 degrees

Practice 18

a. Yes
b. No
c. $-\frac{7}{10}$
d. -16
e. 80,000 mice

Problem Set 18

1. True
2. True
3. Yes
4. No
5. Yes
6. -7
7. -34
8. 7.6
9. -2
10. $-\frac{7}{4}$
11. -6
12. 21
13. 9
14. $\frac{5}{6}$
15. -56.7
16. 9
17. 4
18. 0
19. $\frac{11}{2}$
20. 110,000 bedbugs

Practice 19

a. No
b. -6
c. 24
d. $\frac{5}{6}$
e. $550

Problem Set 19

1. True
2. False
3. Yes
4. No
5. No
6. Yes
7. $\frac{12}{13}$
8. -1
9. 1,000
10. -23
11. $-\frac{4}{5}$
12. -5
13. -9
14. 15
15. 125
16. -15.3
17. $\frac{5}{8}$
18. -73
19. -30
20. $-\frac{2}{7}$
21. $-\frac{11}{56}$
22. $71

CHAPTER 3

Practice 20

a. B
b. 30
c. D
d. C
e. 40 times

Problem Set 20

1. -24
2. 13.5
3. -11.2
4. $\frac{1}{5}$
5. 6
6. -4
7. E
8. E
9. B
10. A
11. C
12. B
13. 17
14. 90
15. -101
16. C
17. E
18. Yes
19. Yes
20. -1
21. $\frac{2}{7}$
22. $\frac{11}{8}$
23. 78,550 people

Practice 21

a. B
b. 22
c. E
d. B
e. C

Problem Set 21

1. B
2. C
3. C
4. -7
5. 10
6. 26
7. E
8. A
9. D
10. B
11. B
12. C
13. A
14. $-\frac{5}{6}$
15. $-\frac{5}{8}$
16. 7.1
17. 0.975
18. 22
19. D

Practice 22

a. B
b. D
c. E
d. C
e. B

Problem Set 22

1. True
2. True
3. C
4. A
5. C
6. A
7. B
8. 2
9. 5
10. -107
11. C
12. A
13. E
14. A
15. A
16. B
17. C
18. $-\frac{7}{15}$
19. $-\frac{1}{7}$
20. $-\frac{5}{4}$
21. D

Practice 23

a. 7
b. Yes
c. Yes
d. 2
e. 7 hours

Problem Set 23

1. True
2. False
3. 12
4. -11
5. 45
6. 4
7. -16.25
8. -2
9. Yes
10. Yes
11. B
12. E
13. A
14. 2
15. 5
16. -30
17. -3
18. 60
19. 32
20. 10 hours

Practice 24

a. −5
b. Yes
c. B
d. 65
e. $100,000

Problem Set 24

1. −1
2. 0
3. 12
4. −2
5. 1
6. 6
7. Yes
8. Yes
9. D
10. B
11. A
12. C
13. B
14. A
15. 39
16. 177
17. 3
18. −5
19. −16
20. 112
21. $1,000,000

Practice 25

a. C
b. D
c. −4
d. 14
e. 40 hours

Problem Set 25

1. B
2. A
3. C
4. 16
5. −6
6. −13
7. −24
8. 118
9. B
10. A
11. B
12. E
13. D
14. C
15. 9
16. 56
17. −5
18. 17
19. 18
20. 25
21. 50 hours

Practice 26

a. D
b. B
c. Yes
d. 10
e. $11

Problem Set 26

1. True
2. True
3. 13
4. 8
5. −1
6. E
7. A
8. B
9. D
10. C
11. Yes
12. No
13. −3
14. 11
15. −12
16. 90
17. 67
18. −11
19. 20
20. 3
21. $18

Practice 27

a. E
b. B
c. 5
d. −2
e. 7%

Problem Set 27

1. E
2. D
3. B
4. A
5. C
6. E
7. Yes
8. No
9. No
10. No
11. 16
12. −8
13. −2
14. −1
15. 5
16. −17
17. 4
18. −180
19. 191,102 words

CHAPTER 4

Practice 28

a. -19
b. E
c. 7
d. 9
e. 8 minutes

Problem Set 28

1. False
2. True
3. True
4. True
5. -26
6. -35
7. D
8. B
9. E
10. A
11. B
12. E
13. 2
14. 4
15. 18
16. 3
17. 5
18. -1
19. 10
20. 44
21. -6
22. 520 minutes

Practice 29

a. Yes
b. No
c. $\frac{1}{2}$ tooth per minute
d. 4
e. 60 minutes

Problem Set 29

1. True
2. True
3. True
4. C
5. E
6. C
7. A
8. D
9. B
10. Yes
11. No
12. Yes
13. $\frac{1}{3}$ turkey per hour
14. $\frac{1}{50}$ banister per minute
15. 48
16. $\frac{3}{5}$
17. -2
18. 11
19. 13
20. -23
21. 9
22. 12 seconds

Practice 30

a. 40 doodles per hour
b. B
c. Yes
d. 3
e. 8 hours

Problem Set 30

1. False
2. True
3. $\frac{1}{15}$ of a batch per minute
4. $\frac{1}{3}$ water pumps per hour
5. 25 parts per hour
6. D
7. E
8. A
9. D
10. E
11. No
12. Yes
13. No
14. 100
15. -150
16. 13
17. -16
18. 0
19. 2
20. 8
21. 10 hours

Practice 31

a. C
b. E
c. -15
d. 6
e. $300

Problem Set 31

1. 41
2. 2
3. -10
4. D
5. E
6. B
7. B
8. A
9. B
10. $\frac{14}{5}$ per hour
11. $\frac{x}{2}$ per hour
12. -23
13. 3
14. $\frac{13}{7}$

15. 12
16. 6
17. 7
18. 3
19. 6
20. 2
21. $80

Practice 32

a. E
b. -15
c. -11
d. $-\frac{9}{2}$
e. $375

Problem Set 32

1. 11
2. 30
3. -25
4. B
5. E
6. A
7. E
8. B
9. Yes
10. No
11. Yes
12. -16
13. -40
14. 0
15. -5
16. 22
17. 2
18. 6
19. 12
20. 17
21. $45

CHAPTER 5

Practice 33

a. 48 both ways
b. E
c. Yes
d. 3
e. 50 times

Problem Set 33

1. True
2. True
3. 14 both ways
4. 35 both ways
5. 28 both ways
6. B
7. E
8. D
9. Yes
10. Yes
11. No
12. Yes
13. 4
14. -48
15. -2
16. 8
17. 12
18. 9
19. -5
20. 3
21. 55 dots

Practice 34

a. 51 both ways
b. D
c. B
d. 9
e. Swimming pool: $5,000; Caribbean: $15,000

Problem Set 34

1. True
2. True
3. 35 both ways
4. 34 both ways
5. -7 both ways
6. D
7. A
8. B
9. E
10. E
11. Yes
12. Yes
13. Yes
14. 6
15. 11
16. 2
17. $\frac{1}{4}$
18. 19
19. -1
20. 12
21. 1
22. Single mucho: $5.50; double mucho: $6.50

Practice 35

a. 5
b. E
c. No
d. $\frac{11}{2}$
e. 18 lions

Problem Set 35

1. True
2. True
3. -5
4. 14
5. -3
6. -63
7. C
8. E
9. B
10. E
11. Yes
12. Yes
13. Yes
14. -75
15. -10
16. 10
17. -16
18. 8
19. $\frac{1}{2}$
20. $-\frac{3}{4}$
21. 48 Siamese cats

Practice 36

a. -2
b. C
c. No
d. 2
e. 60 mph

Problem Set 36

1. -4
2. 28
3. 5
4. D
5. D
6. E
7. B
8. E
9. A
10. No
11. No
12. 72
13. $\frac{2}{7}$
14. 6
15. 2
16. 1
17. 3

18. 7
19. 45
20. 6
21. 75 mph

Practice 37

a. A
b. 20
c. D
d. -3
e. 13 years

Problem Set 37

1. False
2. True
3. True
4. A
5. B
6. D
7. B
8. C
9. -63
10. 27
11. C
12. E
13. A
14. B
15. E
16. 1
17. 8
18. 3
19. 21
20. 15
21. 85
22. 4 years

Practice 38

a. B
b. B
c. E
d. $-\frac{10}{3}$
e. 3.6 minutes

Problem Set 38

1. E
2. B
3. E
4. D
5. -100
6. -32
7. 30
8. B
9. E
10. D
11. No
12. Yes
13. Yes
14. 6
15. 16
16. 9
17. 2
18. -24
19. 4
20. 6
21. $\frac{13}{8}$
22. 10.8 seconds

Practice 39

a. E
b. 6
c. 12
d. -19
e. 11 years

Problem Set 39

1. E
2. A
3. D
4. C
5. 53
6. 6
7. D
8. C
9. B
10. Yes
11. No
12. Yes
13. 7
14. 60
15. 16
16. -3
17. -22
18. 16
19. 8
20. 7
21. 2
22. 35 weeks

CHAPTER 6

Practice 40

a. E
b. D
c. Yes
d. 2
e. 3 hours

Problem Set 40

1. False
2. True
3. True
4. 172
5. -14
6. 84
7. D
8. B
9. B
10. Yes
11. No
12. No
13. $\frac{1}{5}$
14. 8
15. 9
16. 2
17. $-\frac{3}{11}$
18. 8
19. -2
20. $\frac{3}{2}$
21. 5
22. 1 hour

Practice 41

a. 3
b. B
c. $-\frac{9}{2}$
d. -2
e. $750,000

Problem Set 41

1. False
2. True
3. 4
4. -26
5. E
6. C
7. D
8. A
9. D
10. Yes
11. Yes
12. 5
13. 4
14. 20
15. 18
16. 6
17. -35
18. 3
19. $\frac{4}{17}$
20. $1,000,000

Practice 42

a. C
b. E
c. $-\frac{32}{5}$
d. -3
e. 5 seconds

Problem Set 42

1. 2
2. 5
3. -26
4. D
5. B
6. E
7. E
8. B
9. E
10. 6
11. $-\frac{55}{7}$
12. -25
13. 2
14. 1
15. 7
16. 5
17. 8
18. 100
19. 20 seconds

Practice 43

a. B
b. Yes
c. Yes
d. 14
e. 14 pounds

Problem Set 43

1. 2
2. -7
3. D
4. B
5. A
6. E
7. C
8. No
9. Yes
10. Yes
11. $-\frac{1}{2}$
12. $\frac{52}{5}$ or 10.4
13. -2
14. -1
15. 5
16. $\frac{17}{3}$
17. 40
18. $\frac{10}{3}$
19. 12
20. 4 pounds

Practice 44

a. C
b. D
c. Yes
d. $-\frac{6}{11}$
e. 320 pounds

Problem Set 44

1. $\frac{5}{4}$
2. -3
3. -60
4. B
5. A
6. E
7. D
8. B
9. No
10. No
11. Yes
12. $\frac{11}{2}$
13. -2
14. 18
15. 16
16. 9
17. $\frac{21}{2}$
18. 9
19. -2
20. 10 ounces

Practice 45

a. C
b. 2
c. 30
d. 2
e. 600 minutes

Problem Set 45

1. True
2. True
3. -15.82
4. 189
5. A
6. E
7. C
8. B
9. D
10. 4
11. 10
12. -2
13. $\frac{15}{2}$
14. $-\frac{11}{20}$
15. 18
16. $-\frac{5}{2}$
17. $-\frac{7}{4}$
18. $-\frac{8}{5}$
19. 90 minutes

Practice 46

a. E
b. Identity
c. False equation
d. -2
e. 4 hours

Problem Set 46

1. True
2. True
3. D
4. D
5. E
6. A
7. B
8. Yes
9. Yes
10. Identity
11. 4
12. 8
13. $-\frac{15}{2}$
14. $\frac{13}{15}$
15. False equation
16. 21
17. $-\frac{11}{2}$
18. -1
19. 2 hours

CHAPTER 7

Practice 47

a. $\frac{3}{8}$
b. E
c. C
d. $-\frac{54}{25}$
e. 2 hours

Problem Set 47

1. True
2. True
3. False
4. True
5. $\frac{2}{5}$
6. $\frac{2}{7}$
7. $\frac{5}{9}$
8. $\frac{3}{4}$
9. B
10. D
11. E
12. A
13. Yes
14. Yes
15. $\frac{7}{12}$
16. -14
17. 21
18. -3
19. False equation
20. $\frac{25}{6}$
21. $-\frac{15}{14}$
22. $\frac{24}{13}$
23. 10 hours

Practice 48

a. $2\cdot3\cdot3\cdot3$
b. $-\frac{3}{7}$
c. C
d. A
e. 20 milliliters

Problem Set 48

1. False
2. True
3. $2\cdot2\cdot3\cdot5$
4. $2\cdot2\cdot2\cdot3$
5. $2\cdot2\cdot3\cdot3$
6. $2\cdot2\cdot2\cdot7$
7. $3\cdot3\cdot3\cdot3$
8. $\frac{2}{3}$
9. 12
10. $-\frac{5}{4}$
11. $\frac{7}{15}$
12. B
13. D
14. E
15. C
16. Yes
17. No
18. 1
19. 30
20. 3
21. $\frac{1}{4}$
22. -4
23. 20 ounces

Practice 49

a. $-\frac{5}{9}$
b. C
c. D
d. $\frac{8}{7}$
e. $1.50

Problem Set 49

1. False
2. True
3. $-1\cdot2\cdot3\cdot5$
4. $5\cdot5\cdot7$
5. $2\cdot11\cdot x$
6. $-1\cdot3\cdot5\cdot x$
7. $-\frac{1}{2}$
8. $-\frac{4}{5}$
9. $-\frac{9}{13}$
10. E
11. A
12. D
13. E
14. D
15. E
16. $\frac{12}{5}$
17. -126
18. -10
19. 2
20. 0
21. 1
22. False equation
23. -14
24. $2.50

Practice 50

a. B
b. E

c. C
d. 4
e. 7 years

Problem Set 50

1. True
2. True
3. $2 \cdot 2 \cdot 2 \cdot 3 \cdot 3$
4. $-1 \cdot 2 \cdot 3 \cdot 3 \cdot 5 \cdot x$
5. $2 \cdot 2 \cdot 5 \cdot 7 \cdot x$
6. $-1 \cdot 5 \cdot 7 \cdot 11 \cdot y$
7. B
8. E
9. A
10. E
11. D
12. B
13. No
14. Yes
15. No
16. $-\frac{21}{2}$
17. 9
18. 22
19. 7
20. -17
21. Identity
22. -2
23. 12 weeks

Practice 51

a. E
b. C
c. E
d. 10
e. 8 pounds

Problem Set 51

1. False
2. True
3. $2 \cdot 3 \cdot x$
4. $-1 \cdot 2 \cdot 2 \cdot 2 \cdot 2 \cdot 3 \cdot x$
5. B
6. D
7. C
8. E
9. B
10. D
11. E
12. A
13. B
14. E
15. B
16. E
17. -5
18. -2
19. 12
20. 2
21. -1
22. 14
23. 50 pounds

Practice 52

a. B
b. A
c. D
d. C
e. 16 hours

Problem Set 52

1. $2 \cdot 2 \cdot 2 \cdot 2 \cdot 2 \cdot 2 \cdot x$
2. $-1 \cdot 3 \cdot 3 \cdot 3 \cdot 3 \cdot y$
3. B
4. D
5. E
6. C
7. D
8. D
9. B
10. E
11. C
12. A
13. B
14. C
15. E
16. D
17. No
18. Yes
19. 8
20. $-\frac{4}{3}$
21. Identity
22. False equation
23. 18 weeks

Practice 53

a. D
b. B
c. E
d. $\frac{5}{3}$
e. 210 seconds

Problem Set 53

1. True
2. False
3. E
4. B
5. E
6. B
7. B
8. D
9. C
10. B
11. E
12. A
13. C
14. E
15. D
16. 2
17. 14
18. 3
19. $\frac{8}{5}$
20. 4
21. 5
22. 3
23. 40 seconds

Practice 54

- **a.** D
- **b.** B
- **c.** D
- **d.** C
- **e.** 1.5 hours

Problem Set 54

1. True
2. True
3. B
4. E
5. A
6. C
7. E
8. B
9. C
10. D
11. A
12. E
13. B
14. B
15. E
16. D
17. No
18. Yes
19. -1
20. -15
21. $\frac{2}{9}$
22. 0.75 hours

Practice 55

- **a.** C
- **b.** A
- **c.** B
- **d.** $\frac{4}{3}$
- **e.** 36 feet

Problem Set 55

1. True
2. False
3. A
4. E
5. D
6. C
7. A
8. E
9. D
10. E
11. B
12. E
13. C
14. B
15. A
16. B
17. 28
18. -9
19. 15
20. 3
21. $\frac{13}{3}$
22. 8 feet

Practice 56

- **a.** E
- **b.** D
- **c.** B
- **d.** C
- **e.** 7.5 pounds

Problem Set 56

1. True
2. True
3. E
4. B
5. D
6. E
7. B
8. E
9. B
10. E
11. C
12. E
13. D
14. B
15. A
16. C
17. E
18. D
19. -5
20. $\frac{2}{13}$
21. $-\frac{8}{5}$
22. 7
23. 16 ounces

CHAPTER 8

Practice 57

a. C
b. E
c. No
d. −12
e. 4 hours

Problem Set 57

1. True
2. True
3. False
4. D
5. D
6. D
7. E
8. C
9. A
10. A
11. B
12. E
13. C
14. A
15. D
16. No
17. No
18. 1.6
19. −25
20. −5
21. 0
22. 1 hour

Practice 58

a. C
b. B
c. No solution
d. $-\frac{14}{5}$
e. \$19,000

Problem Set 58

1. C
2. A
3. E
4. D
5. A
6. B
7. E
8. B
9. B
10. D
11. C
12. D
13. A
14. E
15. Yes
16. No
17. $\frac{4}{55}$
18. No solution
19. $\frac{3}{2}$
20. −3
21. $-\frac{33}{5}$
22. \$10,000

Practice 59

a. $\frac{2}{3}$
b. D
c. A
d. C
e. 37 kisses

Problem Set 59

1. True
2. True
3. $\frac{3}{4}$
4. 5 : 7
5. B
6. E
7. B
8. C
9. B
10. C
11. A
12. E
13. A
14. E
15. B
16. D
17. 5
18. 2
19. 23.2
20. −3
21. $\frac{16}{5}$
22. 0.2
23. 17 mutts

Practice 60

a. E
b. Yes
c. $\frac{2}{3}$
d. $\frac{1}{3}$
e. 6 unstained benches

Problem Set 60

1. True
2. True
3. B
4. A
5. C
6. D
7. B
8. A
9. B
10. E
11. D
12. C
13. D
14. Yes
15. Yes

16. $\frac{5}{24}$
17. $\frac{1}{5}$
18. $\frac{17}{48}$
19. $-\frac{19}{3}$
20. 1
21. 5
22. 4
23. 89 bags

Practice 61

a. 2:3
b. C
c. D
d. $-\frac{32}{15}$
e. \$80,000

Problem Set 61

1. False
2. True
3. $\frac{6}{7}$
4. 1:2
5. A
6. E
7. D
8. B
9. D
10. E
11. E
12. C
13. B
14. E
15. 6
16. $\frac{2}{9}$
17. $\frac{1}{4}$
18. $\frac{10}{9}$
19. $\frac{15}{8}$
20. $-\frac{19}{60}$
21. 3
22. \$50,000

Practice 62

a. E
b. $30x$
c. $-\frac{32}{21}$
d. $\frac{22}{63}$
e. 27 broken collarbones

Problem Set 62

1. True
2. True
3. E
4. D
5. A
6. C
7. B
8. B
9. D
10. C
11. E
12. A
13. $12x$
14. $6y$
15. $72x$
16. $42x$
17. $\frac{14}{45}$
18. -3
19. $-\frac{3}{10}$
20. $\frac{7}{12}$
21. 1
22. $\frac{23}{42}$
23. 220 blabbermouths

Practice 63

a. $36y$
b. E
c. $-\frac{6}{35}$
d. $-\frac{5}{2}$
e. 12 minutes

Problem Set 63

1. B
2. D
3. E
4. E
5. A
6. E
7. E
8. A
9. B
10. $56y$
11. $12x$
12. $10y$
13. $36x$
14. D
15. $-\frac{11}{10}$
16. $\frac{10}{9}$
17. $-\frac{1}{2}$
18. $\frac{2}{9}$
19. 2
20. $-\frac{9}{4}$
21. 17 minutes

CHAPTER 9

Practice 64

a. y^3

b. $\frac{1}{27}$

c. 2.4^2 or 5.76 square centimeters

d. x^3 cubic feet

e. 70 nickels

Problem Set 64

1. True
2. False
3. False
4. 5^2
5. 8^7
6. x^4
7. 81
8. 274.625
9. $\frac{1}{64}$
10. 5.3^2 or 28.09 square centimeters
11. x^2 square inches
12. 14^3 or 2,744 cubic feet
13. y^3 cubic yards
14. B
15. E
16. D
17. C
18. A
19. B
20. -2
21. 3
22. 5
23. -3
24. 60 nickels

Practice 65

a. 2.3×10^{10}

b. E

c. C

d. No solution

e. 50 mph

Problem Set 65

1. True
2. True
3. 5×10^4
4. 8.9×10^5
5. 1.6×10^9
6. 100
7. 125
8. $\frac{1}{16}$
9. 12^2 or 144 square centimeters
10. 3^3 or 27 cubic inches
11. A
12. B
13. D
14. D
15. B
16. E
17. E
18. 7
19. $\frac{14}{43}$
20. 3
21. $-\frac{37}{12}$
22. No solution
23. 60 mph

Practice 66

a. 27

b. E

c. No

d. C

e. 2 ounces

Problem Set 66

1. True
2. False
3. 18
4. -8
5. 3
6. 9
7. $(-8)^2$
8. x^3
9. B
10. D
11. 4×10^6
12. 1.27×10^7
13. 9.05×10^8
14. No
15. Yes
16. D
17. C
18. E
19. E
20. 5
21. $\frac{1}{3}$
22. 9
23. $-\frac{23}{9}$
24. 5 ounces

Practice 67

a. -25

b. D

c. C

d. D

e. 3 years old

Problem Set 67

1. 64
2. -17
3. -64
4. $\left(\frac{1}{7}\right)^3$

5. y^5
6. C
7. 9×10^9
8. 5.3×10^{12}
9. 4.75×10^4
10. B
11. E
12. D
13. E
14. A
15. No
16. No
17. No
18. 1
19. $\frac{11}{5}$
20. $-\frac{23}{3}$
21. $\frac{2}{27}$
22. $-\frac{35}{4}$
23. 6 years old

Practice 68

a. A
b. E
c. A
d. C
e. $670

Problem Set 68

1. True
2. True
3. C
4. B
5. D
6. 1.19×10^6
7. 7.43×10^8
8. 2.6×10^{13}
9. C
10. E
11. C
12. E
13. E
14. D
15. A
16. C
17. B
18. 6
19. $-\frac{2}{9}$
20. $\frac{2}{3}$
21. 3
22. 5
23. $52

Practice 69

a. E
b. A
c. B
d. C
e. 15 dimes

Problem Set 69

1. 13
2. -7
3. E
4. C
5. A
6. 5^2
7. 4^3
8. 2.854×10^4
9. 2.7×10^9
10. 9.999×10^{11}
11. A
12. E
13. A
14. B
15. C
16. B
17. E
18. -70
19. 1
20. -28
21. $-\frac{18}{25}$
22. 4
23. 200 dimes

Practice 70

a. x^3
b. y
c. $\frac{1}{x^5}$
d. Yes
e. 9 hours

Problem Set 70

1. True
2. False
3. True
4. -6
5. -2
6. y^8
7. x^9
8. x^4
9. z
10. $\frac{1}{y^7}$
11. E
12. B
13. C
14. A
15. Yes
16. Yes
17. Yes
18. -1
19. $\frac{27}{2}$
20. 6
21. $-\frac{5}{17}$
22. $\frac{20}{13}$

23. $-\frac{16}{7}$
24. 2 hours

Practice 71
a. 4.52×10^{-8}
b. 1.5×10^{15}
c. 2×10^{-2}
d. C
e. 78

Problem Set 71
1. False
2. True
3. -13
4. -11
5. 5×10^{-4}
6. 8.3×10^{-6}
7. 6.97×10^{-8}
8. 1.6×10^{18}
9. 3×10^{-3}
10. x^{11}
11. y^{10}
12. x
13. $\frac{1}{x^2}$
14. B
15. D
16. E
17. D
18. D
19. $\frac{22}{5}$
20. $\frac{1}{8}$
21. -9
22. -3
23. -4
24. 1,002

Practice 72
a. A
b. C
c. B
d. E
e. $50,000

Problem Set 72
1. 9.73×10^{11}
2. 4.19×10^{-8}
3. 1.28×10^{23}
4. 3.2×10^{-10}
5. x^{12}
6. x^7
7. $\frac{1}{y^7}$
8. E
9. D
10. C
11. A
12. C
13. E
14. E
15. A
16. D
17. E
18. $\frac{5}{3}$
19. $\frac{34}{9}$
20. $-\frac{21}{8}$
21. 3
22. -27
23. $100,000

Practice 73
a. B
b. C
c. D
d. A
e. 1,224 busybodies

Problem Set 73
1. 8
2. 5
3. 0
4. E
5. C
6. A
7. D
8. C
9. E
10. D
11. A
12. E
13. B
14. D
15. A
16. A
17. -9
18. $-\frac{2}{3}$
19. $\frac{51}{2}$
20. 2
21. $-\frac{41}{24}$
22. 235 natural tans

CHAPTER 10

Practice 74
a. 6
b. 2
c. $\frac{1}{2}$
d. B
e. 2 seconds

Problem Set 74
1. True
2. True
3. 7
4. 28
5. 4
6. 3
7. -30
8. $\frac{1}{3}$
9. D
10. D
11. E
12. A
13. E
14. B
15. E
16. E
17. 4
18. -1
19. 13
20. 3
21. 2
22. 4 hours

Practice 75
a. 7
b. 11
c. B
d. 3
e. 4.5 ounces

Problem Set 75
1. True
2. True
3. True
4. 10
5. 5
6. 14
7. 22
8. E
9. D
10. C
11. D
12. E
13. B
14. Yes
15. No
16. $-\frac{50}{9}$
17. 4
18. 2
19. $-\frac{32}{21}$
20. 8
21. 3
22. 2.4 ounces

Practice 76
a. Irrational
b. $\sqrt[3]{50}$
c. D
d. $-\frac{85}{11}$
e. 11 years

Problem Set 76
1. True
2. True
3. 4
4. 9
5. 7
6. Irrational
7. Rational
8. Rational
9. Irrational
10. $\sqrt{3}$
11. $\sqrt{15}$
12. 4
13. 5.5×10^{-5}
14. 1.2×10^{10}
15. 1.08×10^{-7}
16. C
17. A
18. A
19. E
20. 123
21. 512
22. 1
23. $-\frac{45}{7}$
24. 5 years

Practice 77
a. 2.83
b. B
c. E
d. -4
e. 52

Problem Set 77
1. True
2. False
3. Irrational
4. Rational
5. Irrational
6. 2.65
7. 3.87
8. 4.36
9. 4.58
10. D
11. B
12. A
13. $\sqrt{30}$
14. 4.75
15. $-\sqrt{2}$
16. D

17. E
18. D
19. B
20. 1
21. 0.0001
22. 0
23. -3
24. 26

Practice 78

a. 26
b. 25.38
c. E
d. B
e. 32 quarters

Problem Set 78

1. False
2. True
3. False
4. 13
5. 4
6. 12.69
7. $\sqrt{6}$
8. $\sqrt{\frac{1}{4}}$
9. D
10. E
11. C
12. A
13. E
14. D
15. C
16. A
17. -5
18. 4
19. 18
20. 2
21. 3
22. 48 dimes

CHAPTER 11

Practice 79

a. C
b. E
c. B
d. D
e. 40 minutes

Problem Set 79

1. True
2. False
3. True
4. B
5. C
6. A
7. 9
8. -1
9. 2.625×10^{14}
10. 3×10^{-4}
11. B
12. D
13. A
14. E
15. E
16. B
17. D
18. 1
19. -7
20. $\frac{6}{11}$
21. B
22. C
23. 180 seconds

Practice 80

a. D
b. A
c. E
d. D
e. 23 wallflowers

Problem Set 80

1. False
2. False
3. B
4. C
5. D
6. C
7. D
8. E
9. B
10. E
11. C
12. E
13. A
14. D
15. E
16. Yes
17. No
18. 1
19. 4
20. B
21. D
22. C
23. B
24. 23 bumblers

Practice 81

a. Factoring
b. $x=0,\ x=-4$
c. $x=4.36,$
$x=-4.36$
d. $x=0,\ x=-6$
e. 13 hours

Problem Set 81

1. D
2. A
3. 3.8×10^{9}
4. 7.7×10^{-8}
5. 6.92×10^{14}
6. 5.74
7. 6.40
8. 5.39
9. Undoing
10. Factoring
11. Factoring
12. $x=0,\ x=1$
13. $x=0,\ x=7$
14. $x=0,\ x=-6$
15. E
16. D
17. -55
18. 1
19. $x=2,\ x=-4$
20. $x=3.87,\ x=-3.87$
21. $x=0,\ x=3$
22. $x=0,\ x=-5$
23. 11 hours

Practice 82

a. $x=3,\ x=-1$
b. $x=7.36,\ x=-1.36$
c. $x=0,\ x=\frac{1}{3}$
d. $x=7,\ x=3$
e. 11 years

Problem Set 82

1. $\frac{1}{5}$
2. -11
3. 14
4. 6
5. $\sqrt{\frac{1}{9}}$
6. 10
7. 8.06
8. $x=0,\ x=-8$
9. $x=1,\ x=6$
10. $x=2,\ x=-3$
11. C
12. E
13. B
14. E

15. A
16. E
17. $-\frac{16}{3}$
18. 0
19. $x=5,\ x=-5$
20. $x=7.61,\ x=0.39$
21. $x=0,\ x=\frac{1}{2}$
22. $x=9,\ x=2$
23. 8 years

Practice 83

a. D
b. $x=5,\ x=-1$
c. $x=-3,\ x=-4$
d. $x=7,\ x=4$
e. 5 seconds

Problem Set 83

1. True
2. True
3. C
4. B
5. C
6. D
7. E
8. $x=0,\ x=13$
9. $x=9,\ x=-1$
10. C
11. E
12. Yes
13. No
14. -6
15. 2
16. $-\frac{18}{5}$
17. $x=3,\ x=-3$
18. $x=18,\ x=6$
19. $x=-2,\ x=-1$
20. $x=-5,\ x=-2$
21. $x=7,\ x=3$
22. 4 seconds

Practice 84

a. C
b. $x=2.24,$ $x=-2.24$
c. $x=0,\ x=16$
d. $x=5,\ x=-3$
e. \$3,125

Problem Set 84

1. True
2. False
3. E
4. A
5. D
6. D
7. C
8. B
9. E
10. E
11. B
12. A
13. 9
14. 7
15. -4
16. $x=2.16,$ $x=-4.16$
17. $x=2.65,$ $x=-2.65$
18. $x=0,\ x=-7$
19. $x=0,\ x=15$
20. $x=-7,\ x=-2$
21. $x=6,\ x=-4$
22. \$6,000

Practice 85

a. B
b. D
c. $x=0.32,\ x=-6.32$
d. $x=11.24,\ x=-1.24$
e. 20 ounces

Problem Set 85

1. True
2. True
3. 20
4. -10
5. 7.62
6. -8.43
7. B
8. D
9. E
10. B
11. A
12. C
13. E
14. -15
15. $-\frac{1}{10}$
16. $x=6,\ x=2$
17. $x=0,\ x=-4$
18. $x=0.36,\ x=-8.36.$
19. $x=13.28,\ x=-1.28$
20. 15 milliliters

Practice 86

a. D
b. $x=8,\ x=6$
c. $x=0.16,\ x=-6.16$
d. $x=0.74,\ x=-4.74$
e. 160 seconds

Problem Set 86

1. -18
2. 9
3. A
4. E
5. C
6. E
7. C

8. 10.25
9. 8.06
10. B
11. E
12. A
13. B
14. 47
15. 7
16. $x = 0,\ x = 8$
17. $x = 7,\ x = 5$
18. $x = 0.24,\ x = -4.24$
19. $x = 0.68,\ x = -3.68$
20. 4,200 seconds

CHAPTER 12

Practice 87

a. $y=-5$
b. Yes
c. D
d. $x=3,\ x=-2$
e. 23 quarters

Problem Set 87

1. True
2. True
3. True
4. 3
5. 48
6. 9
7. $y=7$
8. $y=13$
9. $y=1$
10. $y=4$
11. No
12. Yes
13. No
14. Yes
15. B
16. E
17. No
18. Yes
19. -3
20. -1
21. $x=4,\ x=1$
22. $x=2,\ x=-1$
23. 16 dimes

Practice 88

a. $x=11,\ x=-4$
b. D
c. B
d. C
e. 22 molded vegetables

Problem Set 88

1. True
2. True
3. 1.302×10^{18}
4. 4×10^{4}
5. $y=-3$
6. $y=1$
7. $y=-\frac{5}{3}$
8. No
9. Yes
10. Yes
11. B
12. A
13. 9
14. $-\frac{91}{2}$
15. $x=0,\ x=-6$
16. $x=11,\ x=-3$
17. A
18. E
19. D
20. C
21. B
22. D
23. 11 gigantic rats

Practice 89

a. E
b. $x=4.27,\ x=0.23$
c. A
d. C
e. 6,375 devices

Problem Set 89

1. 6
2. 44
3. 5
4. 15
5. 1
6. 3
7. D

8. E
9. C
10. $y = 27$
11. $y = 16$
12. No
13. Yes
14. D
15. A
16. $y = -0.68,\ y = -7.32$
17. $x = 0,\ x = -1$
18. $x = 2.37,\ x = 0.63$
19. C
20. E
21. A
22. 2,123 pairs

Practice 90

a.

y=5x+2

x	-2	-1	0	1	2	3
y	-8	-3	2	7	12	17

b. 208 feet per second
c. 676 feet
d. 7.9 seconds
e. 33

Problem Set 90

1. True
2. True
3. 19
4. -1
5. B
6. E
7. B
8. C
9. $\frac{9}{5}$
10. 10
11. $x = 0,\ x = 2$
12. $x = -7,\ x = -6$
13. $x = 6,\ x = 3$
14.

y=x-2

x	-2	-1	0	1	2	3
y	-4	-3	-2	-1	0	1

15.

y=3x+4

x	-2	-1	0	1	2	3
y	-2	1	4	7	10	13

16. 144 feet per second
17. 324 feet
18. 7.7 seconds
19. D
20. E
21. C
22. 49

Practice 91

a. C
b. E
c. $x = 2.15,\ x = -0.15$
d. 3.4 seconds
e. 2 hours

Problem Set 91

1. True
2. True
3. -2
4. -4
5. C
6. E
7. C
8. B
9. D
10. C
11. 4
12. 1
13. $x = 4,\ x = -3$
14. $x = 2.22,\ x = -0.22$

15.

$y=4x+1$

x	-2	-1	0	1	2	3
y	-7	-3	1	5	9	13

16.

$y=15-3x$

x	-2	-1	0	1	2	3
y	21	18	15	12	9	6

17. 92.8 feet per second
18. 2.7 seconds
19. B
20. E
21. C
22. 3 hours

Practice 92

a. B
b. $A=25$
c.

$z=x+2y$

x	-2	-1	0	1	2	3
y	0	1	2	3	4	5
z	-2	1	4	7	10	13

d. D
e. 8 percussionists

Problem Set 92

1. True
2. True
3. C
4. E
5. D
6. A
7. C
8. Yes
9. No
10. -2
11. 15
12. $x=2,\ x=-2$
13. $x=1.74,\ x=-5.74$
14. $A=24$
15. 9.5 seconds
16.

$y=\frac{1}{4}x$

x	-2	-1	0	1	2	3
y	$-\frac{1}{2}$	$-\frac{1}{4}$	0	$\frac{1}{4}$	$\frac{1}{2}$	$\frac{3}{4}$

17.

$z=2x+3y$

x	-2	-1	0	1	2	3
y	0	1	2	3	4	5
z	-4	1	6	11	16	21

18. A
19. C
20. E
21. 32 fauvists

Practice 93

a. E
b. $y=4,\ y=1$
c. $V=378$
d. D
e. 9 years ago

Problem Set 93

1. True
2. False
3. True
4. 9
5. 1
6. D
7. C
8. E
9. C
10. 6
11. 2
12. $x=4,\ x=-9$
13. $y=3,\ y=1$

14.

2x+3y=5

x	5.5	4	2.5	1	-0.5	-2
y	-2	-1	0	1	2	3

15.

z=5y-x

x	3	2	1	0	-1	-2
y	5	4	3	2	1	0
z	22	18	14	10	6	2

16. $P=40$

17. $V=294.4$

18. A

19. B

20. 12 years ago

CHAPTER 13

Practice 94

a. B
b. D
c. E
d. C
e. 6

Problem Set 94

1. True
2. True
3. −13
4. 5
5. C
6. D
7. B
8. E
9. A
10. B
11. 9
12. $-\frac{1}{3}$
13. $x=8,\ x=0$
14. $x=7,\ x=4$
15. Yes
16. No
17. Yes
18. E
19. A
20. C
21. 11

Practice 95

a. E
b. C
c. No
d. A
e. 65 adults

Problem Set 95

1. D
2. E
3. C
4. A
5. D
6. C
7. B
8. D
9. No
10. Yes
11. 9
12. −3
13. $x=0,\ x=3$
14. $x=4,\ x=1$
15.

4y-3x=1

x	-2	-1	0	1	2	3
y	-1.25	-0.5	0.25	1	1.75	2.5

16.

z=5xy

x	-2	-1	0	1	2	3
y	3	4	5	6	7	8
z	-30	-20	0	30	70	120

17. $z=7$
18. $B=72$
19. C
20. A
21. 98 adults

Practice 96

a. A
b. B
c. E
d. $x=7.12,\ x=-1.12$
e. 50 mph

Problem Set 96

1. True
2. True
3. 17

4. 21
5. -12
6. B
7. D
8. C
9. E
10. A
11. C
12. C
13. -5
14. 24
15. $x=5.61,\ x=-1.61$
16. $z=-2$
17. $\lambda=0.025$ or $\frac{1}{40}$
18. $T=100$
19. D
20. D
21. 55 mph

Practice 97

a. D
b. E
c. $x=-1.42,\ x=-10.58$
d. B
e. $30,000

Problem Set 97

1. 8
2. 20
3. D
4. E
5. C
6. A
7. E
8. D
9. No
10. Yes
11. -7
12. 2
13. $x=1.73,\ x=-1.73$
14. $x=-3.68,\ x=-10.32$
15. $z=5$
16. $V=64$
17. B
18. E
19. C
20. $3,000

Practice 98

a. D
b. E
c. E
d. $x=7,\ x=-6$
e. 50 mph

Problem Set 98

1. 8.63×10^{12}
2. 7.05×10^{-5}
3. B
4. E
5. B
6. E
7. D
8. B
9. C
10. E
11. C
12. $\frac{1}{11}$
13. 8
14. $z=0,\ z=-\frac{1}{2}$
15. $x=8,\ x=-7$
16. No
17. Yes
18.

y=2x-5

x	-2	-1	0	1	2	3
y	-9	-7	-5	-3	-1	1

19.

y-3x=9

x	-2	-1	0	1	2	3
y	3	6	9	12	15	18

20. 54 mph

Practice 99

a. D
b. B
c. C
d. E
e. 35 nickels

Problem Set 99

1. E
2. A
3. B
4. C
5. E
6. A
7. E
8. D
9. E
10. A
11. C
12. 10
13. -3
14. $x=-5,\ x=-11$
15. $x=2.24,\ x=-2.24$
16. $z=13$
17. $A=1{,}140$
18. B
19. E
20. 8 dimes

Practice 100

a. B
b. E
c. D
d. C
e. \$1.50

Problem Set 100

1. True
2. False
3. -88
4. -2
5. B
6. E
7. D
8. A
9. C
10. C
11. E
12. E
13. D
14. E
15. B
16. -68
17. $\frac{14}{103}$
18. $x=0,\ x=\frac{1}{2}$
19. $x=7,\ x=-1$
20. \$200

Practice 101

a. E
b. B
c. C
d. E
e. 14 snow globes

Problem Set 101

1. 4
2. 44
3. A
4. D
5. A
6. C
7. D
8. B
9. A
10. E
11. D
12. No
13. Yes
14. -7
15. $-\frac{11}{2}$
16. $p=48$
17. $I=12$

18. B
19. D
20. 23 messages

Practice 102

a. D
b. A
c. C
d. B
e. 100 seconds

Problem Set 102

1. 7
2. 4
3. D
4. E
5. B
6. B
7. D
8. E
9. D
10. 6
11. $\frac{6}{5}$
12. $x=5.58,\ x=-3.58$
13. $x=2.65,\ x=-2.65$
14.

y=-4x+1

x	-2	-1	0	1	2	3
y	9	5	1	-3	-7	-11

15.

y-x=8

x	-2	-1	0	1	2	3
y	6	7	8	9	10	11

16. $x=4$
17. $r=68.5$
18. C
19. E
20. 480 seconds

Practice 103

a. C
b. D
c. D
d. E
e. 73

Problem Set 103

1. True
2. False
3. 4.58×10^{-5}
4. 6.5×10^{9}
5. 1.4×10^{-10}
6. A
7. C
8. A
9. C
10. B
11. E
12. D
13. E
14. C
15. Yes
16. No
17. -6
18. -10
19. 2
20. A
21. C
22. 91

Practice 104

a. E
b. B
c. B
d. E
e. 1.2 hours

Problem Set 104

1. 8
2. 16
3. -8
4. 3.32

5. -5.92
6. A
7. D
8. E
9. D
10. E
11. B
12. E
13. D
14. C
15. $x = 0,\ x = -2$
16. $x = 3,\ x = -4$
17. A
18. E
19. B
20. 4.5 hours

CHAPTER 14

Practice 105

a.

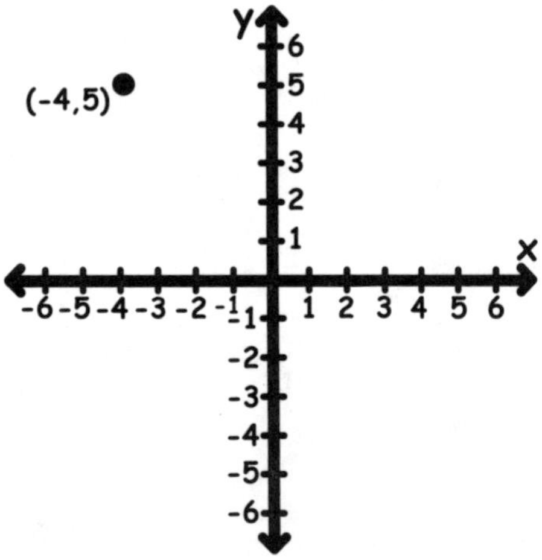

b. B
c. C
d. E
e. \$9,250,000

Problem Set 105

1. True
2. True
3. True
4. False
5. True

6. through 8.

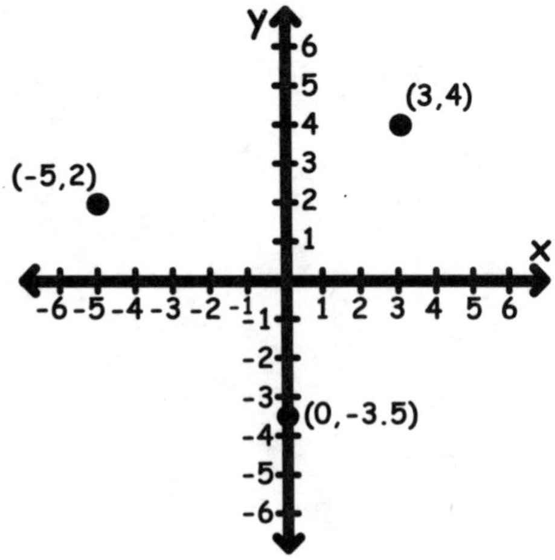

9. D
10. C
11. C
12. E
13. D
14. E
15. A
16. $\frac{24}{7}$
17. 3
18. -1
19. $x = 8$
20. C
21. \$3,845,000

Practice 106

a. D
b. A
c. D
d. A
e. 6 years old

Problem Set 106

1. True
2. True
3. True

4. – 6.

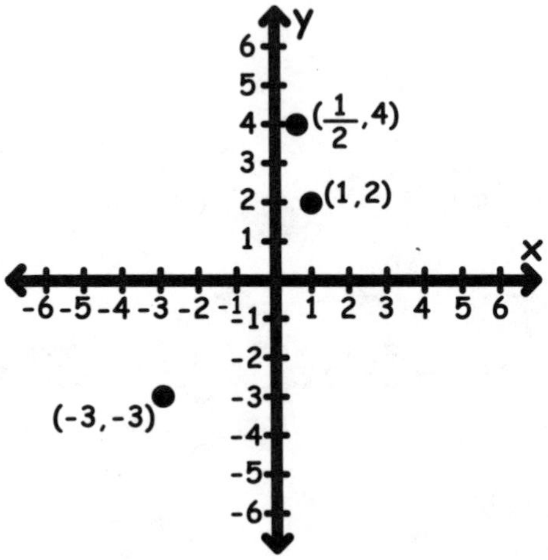

7. 2.9×10^{7}
8. 5.8×10^{-6}
9. 1.04×10^{11}
10. E
11. E

12. E
13. C
14. -4
15. $\frac{3}{2}$
16. $y=4$
17. $y=-8$
18. $z=-3$
19. C
20. B
21. C
22. E
23. 3 years old

Practice 107

a. E
b. B
c. C
d. B
e. 57 penny loafer wearers

Problem Set 107

1. True
2. False
3. and 4.

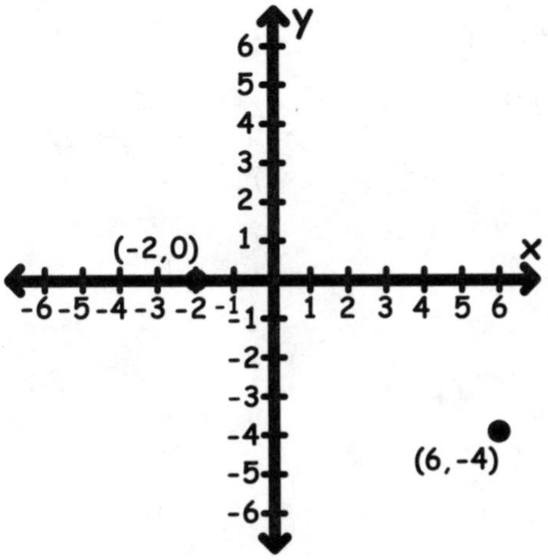

5. C
6. E
7. Yes
8. Yes
9. $\frac{20}{19}$
10. $x=5.57,\ x=-5.57$
11.

$y=\frac{1}{3}x-1$

x	-2	-1	0	1	2	3
y	$-\frac{5}{3}$	$-\frac{4}{3}$	-1	$-\frac{2}{3}$	$-\frac{1}{3}$	0

12.

y-x=2.5

x	0	1	2	3	4	5
y	2.5	3.5	4.5	5.5	6.5	7.5

13. $z=-2$
14. D
15. A
16. D
17. B
18. E
19. D
20. B
21. B
22. 34 hard-boiled skeptics

Practice 108

a. D
b. E
c. $U=87$
d. x-intercept: $(-2,0)$; y-intercept: $(0,8)$
e. 52.5 mph

Problem Set 108

1. False
2. False
3. A
4. D
5. C
6. B
7. C
8. A

9. $y = 0,\ y = 2$
10. $x = 1,\ x = -12$
11. C
12. 20° Celsius
13. 95 ° Fahrenheit
14. B
15. C
16. A
17. x-intercept: $(-7,0)$; y-intercept: $(0,7)$
18. x-intercept: $(-3,0)$; y-intercept: $(0,9)$
19. C
20. E
21. 50 mph

CHAPTER 15

Practice 109

a. C
b. 1
c. 3
d. 2
e. 72 minutes

Problem Set 109

1. True
2. False
3. True
4. A
5. C
6. B
7. D
8. Yes
9. No
10. -63
11. $\frac{33}{29}$
12. $d = 10$
13. E
14. 5
15. 1
16. 2
17. 4
18. 2
19. C
20. D
21. 900 seconds

Practice 110

a. C
b. $-\frac{2}{5}$
c. C
d. B
e. 6 hours

Problem Set 110

1. True
2. True
3. through 5.

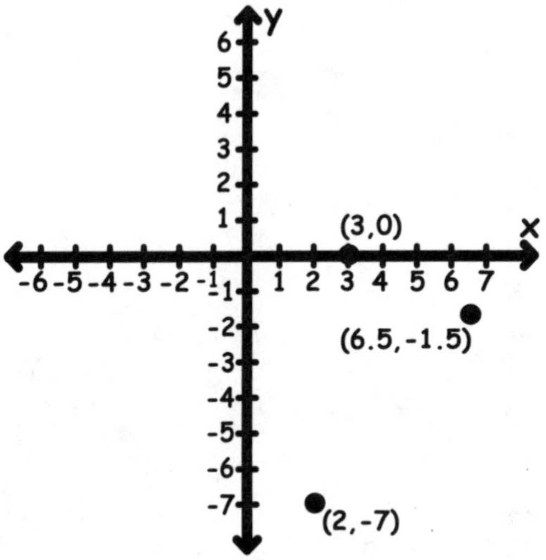

6. B
7. E
8. E
9. A
10. -20
11. $-\frac{1}{3}$
12. -3
13. -2
14. $-\frac{9}{7}$
15. $E = 3$
16. D
17. B
18. D
19. A
20. C
21. 3 hours

Practice 111

a. Undefined
b. $-\frac{1}{3}$
c. C
d. E
e. $12,000

Problem Set 111

1. False
2. False
3. D
4. E
5. B
6. D
7. A
8. D
9. 2
10. 6
11. -14
12. 0
13. Undefined
14. 2
15. $\frac{3}{4}$
16. $-\frac{1}{2}$
17. C
18. A
19. A
20. C
21. \$20,000

Practice 112

a. B

b. Slope: $\frac{3}{7}$; y-intercept: $(0, 0)$

c. Slope: $\frac{1}{2}$; y-intercept: $(0, -7)$

d. E

e. 20 ounces

Problem Set 112

1. True
2. True
3. -15
4. 6
5. E
6. C
7. B
8. D
9. Yes
10. No
11. $-\frac{11}{2}$
12. -62
13. $z = 10$
14. A
15. Slope: -3; y-intercept: $(0, -2)$
16. Slope: $\frac{4}{5}$; y-intercept: $(0, 0)$
17. Slope: $\frac{1}{2}$; y-intercept: $(0, -8)$
18. B
19. D
20. D
21. 4 ounces

Practice 113

a. E

b. A

c. C

d. C

e. \$120,000

Problem Set 113

1. True
2. True
3. C
4. E
5. D
6. C
7. A
8. E
9. $x = 2.65$, $x = -2.65$
10. $x = 8$, $x = -4$
11. $a = 5$
12. C
13. Slope: 4; y-intercept: $(0, -3)$
14. Slope: $\frac{1}{2}$; y-intercept: $(0, 7)$
15. Slope: $\frac{2}{3}$; y-intercept: $(0, -3)$

16. E
17. A
18. C
19. A
20. B
21. A
22. 105 hours

CHAPTER 16

Practice 114
a. C
b. D
c. $x=6$, $y=4$
d. $x=5$, $y=5$
e. 16, 5

Problem Set 114
1. True
2. True
3. D
4. E
5. E
6. D
7. B
8. C
9. 1
10. -9
11. $x=14$
12. A
13. B
14. E
15. D
16. E
17. A
18. $x=3$, $y=5$
19. $x=7$, $y=9$
20. $x=5$, $y=4$
21. 38, 11

Practice 115
a. E
b. A
c. C
d. $x=2$, $y=12$
e. a.) 14 adults
b.) 5 children

Problem Set 115
1. and 2.

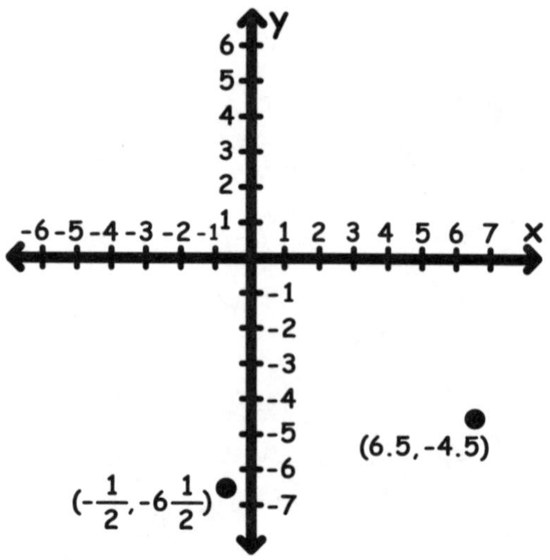

3. B
4. D
5. C
6. A
7. No
8. Yes
9. -166
10. 4
11. $P_2=10$
12. B
13. Slope: -12; y-intercept: $(0,0)$
14. Slope: 2; y-intercept: $(0,\frac{1}{2})$
15. Slope: -3; y-intercept: $(0,\frac{7}{3})$
16. D
17. E
18. $x=-4$, $y=-19$
19. $x=17$, $y=-4$
20. $x=2$, $y=14$
21. a.) 29 adults
b.) 9 children

Practice 116

- **a.** D
- **b.** $-\frac{5}{3}$
- **c.** C
- **d.** $x=2$, $y=2$
- **e.** 5 years old

Problem Set 116

1. -12
2. 3
3. B
4. C
5. D
6. B
7. 28
8. $\frac{33}{16}$
9. $i=2{,}400$
10. A
11. C
12. E
13. -6
14. $\frac{3}{5}$
15. $-\frac{3}{2}$
16. E
17. C
18. $x=1$, $y=-\frac{7}{3}$
19. $x=\frac{1}{2}$, $y=-2$
20. $x=4$, $y=0$
21. 3 years old

Practice 117

- **a.** C
- **b.** D
- **c.** $x=1$, $y=4$
- **d.** $x=4$, $y=2$
- **e.** a.) \$3 for each handkerchief
  b.) \$2.50 for each rubber nose

Problem Set 117

1. 5
2. 27
3. B
4. C
5. D
6. E
7. Yes
8. Yes
9. $x=0$, $x=2$
10. $x=-3$, $x=-2$
11. $y=15$
12. B
13. Slope: -2; y-intercept: $(0,-9)$
14. Slope: 3; y-intercept: $(0,2)$
15. D
16. A
17. $x=2$, $y=5$
18. $x=-1$, $y=-6$
19. $x=-3$, $y=-1$
20. a.) \$1.50 for each jigsaw puzzle
    b.) \$1 for each paddle ball paddle

Practice 118

- **a.** A
- **b.** D
- **c.** D
- **d.** C
- **e.** 92

Problem Set 118

1. True
2. True
3. A
4. E
5. D
6. B
7. 2

8. $-\frac{5}{2}$
9. 5
10. E
11. B
12. E
13. $-\frac{5}{7}$
14. 14
15. -2
16. A
17. C
18. A
19. C
20. D
21. 108

Practice 119

a. Yes
b. E
c. B
d. D
e. 12 years old

Problem Set 119

1. True
2. True
3. E
4. C
5. A
6. E
7. C
8. E
9. Yes
10. No
11. -6
12. 2
13. $z = 9$
14. A
15. Slope: 1; y-intercept: (0,20)
16. Slope: 2; y-intercept: (0,5)
17. C
18. B
19. E
20. 4 years old

CHAPTER 17

Practice 120

a. B
b. C
c. D
d. A
e. 2.5 hours

Problem Set 120

1. False
2. True
3. E
4. D
5. A
6. E
7. A
8. D
9. C
10. D
11. 8
12. $\frac{17}{5}$
13. $f = 26$
14. C
15. B
16. E
17. D
18. C
19. $x = 10$, $y = 2$
20. $x = 2$, $y = 4$
21. 7 hours

Practice 121

a. B
b. C
c. E
d. $x = -2$, $y = 0$
e. 12 socks

Problem Set 121

1. True
2. False
3. B
4. E
5. C
6. E
7. C
8. E
9. $x = 0$, $x = 6$
10. $x = 8$, $x = -4$
11. $k = 45$
12. C
13. $\frac{2}{7}$
14. $\frac{5}{2}$
15. D
16. A
17. B
18. B
19. C
20. $x = 1$, $y = 4$
21. $x = -3$, $y = 0$
22. 103 bugs

Practice 122

a. D
b. A
c. C
d. D
e. 312 people heartily recommended

Problem Set 122

1. E
2. C
3. B
4. A
5. $\frac{25}{7}$
6. 6
7. B

8. E
9. C
10. E
11. $V = 1{,}004.8$
12. B
13. Slope: 13; y-intercept: (0, 4)
14. Slope: $-\frac{1}{8}$; y-intercept: (0, 0)
15. $x = 10$, $y = 30$
16. $x = 2$, $y = 20$
17. B
18. E
19. D
20. B
21. 189 people threw cabbage

Practice 123

a. 6
b. $\sqrt{15}$
c. $\sqrt[4]{12}$
d. E
e. B

Problem Set 123

1. True
2. True
3. B
4. E
5. C
6. C
7. 10
8. $\sqrt{21}$
9. 3
10. $\sqrt[3]{28}$
11. $\sqrt[4]{24}$
12. $\frac{13}{3}$
13. 2
14. $P = 100{,}000$
15. C
16. $x = 2$, $y = 1$
17. $x = 4$, $y = -3$
18. D
19. E
20. C
21. C

Practice 124

a. 2
b. $\sqrt{3}$
c. B
d. $x = 1$, $y = 4$
e. 2,260 adult tickets

Problem Set 124

1. 4
2. $\sqrt{57}$
3. 3
4. 5
5. $\sqrt{5}$
6. A
7. C
8. D
9. E
10. -34
11. 15
12. C
13. E
14. Slope: 4; y-intercept: $(0, 19)$
15. Slope: $\frac{3}{7}$; y-intercept: $(0, 0)$
16. $x = 12$, $y = 16$
17. $x = 0$, $y = 3$
18. D
19. A
20. C
21. 11 mezzanine tickets

Practice 125

a. D
b. B
c. E

d. E
e. C

Problem Set 125

1. True
2. False
3. C
4. A
5. 9
6. $\sqrt[3]{30}$
7. $\sqrt[4]{3}$
8. B
9. E
10. A
11. A
12. B
13. D
14. 4
15. $\dfrac{3}{2}$
16. C
17. C
18. $r=5$
19. D
20. $x=1,\ y=2$
21. $x=3,\ y=6$
22. D

Practice 126

a. $4\sqrt{5}$
b. $2\sqrt[3]{7}$
c. $5\sqrt{2}$
d. C
e. 200 games

Problem Set 126

1. True
2. True
3. $4\sqrt{7}$
4. $2\sqrt[3]{9}$
5. $4\sqrt{2}$
6. $5\sqrt{3}$
7. $\sqrt{2}$
8. Yes
9. No
10. A
11. E
12. $x=4,\ x=0$
13. $x=32$
14. D
15. $x=2,\ y=11$
16. $x=9,\ y=3$
17. B
18. D
19. E
20. 216 seconds

Practice 127

a. A
b. B
c. 0
d. D
e. 7.8 hours

Problem Set 127

1. True
2. True
3. True
4. E
5. C
6. D
7. 3
8. −2
9. 3
10. $k=-\dfrac{3}{2}$
11. A
12. −19
13. 0
14. D
15. C
16. $x=2,\ y=-5$
17. $x=1,\ y=8$

18. $x = \frac{7}{6}$, $y = -\frac{1}{6}$
19. C
20. E
21. 7.2 hours

Practice 128

a. B
b. E
c. A
d. D
e. 348 legislators

Problem Set 128

1. False
2. True
3. C
4. E
5. −1
6. 5
7. E
8. $h = 121$
9. D
10. $\frac{1}{3}$
11. 0
12. C
13. A
14. $x = 2$, $y = -6$
15. $x = 4$, $y = -4$
16. B
17. E
18. E
19. C
20. B
21. C
22. 416 bows

Practice 129

a. D
b. D
c. A
d. D
e. A

Problem Set 129

1. True
2. True
3. 9
4. B
5. A
6. 0, 3
7. −8, 2
8. No
9. No
10. $x = -6$, $y = -8$
11. $x = -1$, $y = -3$
12. C
13. E
14. B
15. A
16. D
17. A
18. E
19. C
20. A
21. D

Practice 130

a. E
b. E
c. A
d. C
e. a.) $2.50
   b.) $4.75

Problem Set 130

1. True
2. False
3. $\sqrt{7}$
4. A
5. C
6. C
7. D
8. 3

9. 100
10. 2
11. E
12. A
13. $x=1,\ y=-5$
14. $x=\frac{1}{2},\ y=-1$
15. B
16. C
17. B
18. C
19. B
20. E
21. a.) $3.50
b.) $5.25

CHAPTER 18

Practice 131

a. 9
b. 6
c. B
d. C
e. 4 years old

Problem Set 131

1. True
2. True
3. 2
4. 6
5. 3
6. 4
7. $-\frac{7}{6}$
8. 2
9. A
10. D
11. $x=-1$, $y=2$
12. $x=0$, $y=-3$
13. D
14. E
15. C
16. A
17. E
18. D
19. C
20. B
21. D
22. 3 years old

Practice 132

a. $x=5.45$, $x=0.55$
b. C
c. $x=7$, $x=-3$
d. $x=2$, $x=-10$
e. 14 plates

Problem Set 132

1. True
2. True
3. 5
4. $\frac{1}{2}$
5. 5
6. C
7. E
8. $x=4$, $x=-3$
9. $x=\frac{1}{5}$, $x=0$
10. $x=3.65$, $x=-1.65$
11. A
12. E
13. $x=-1$, $y=-2$
14. $x=-\frac{1}{3}$, $y=\frac{1}{2}$
15. A
16. E
17. B
18. E
19. $x=2$, $x=-2$
20. $x=4$, $x=-2$
21. $x=2$, $x=-8$
22. 21 seashells

Practice 133

a. E
b. E
c. $x=13$, $x=-8$
d. $x=-4$
e. B

Problem Set 133

1. True
2. True
3. D
4. E
5. $\frac{7}{8}$
6. $-\frac{3}{4}$
7. B
8. D
9. $f=-4$
10. A
11. $\frac{1}{4}$
12. $\frac{5}{3}$
13. C
14. C
15. B
16. C
17. B
18. D
19. $x=17$, $x=-9$
20. $x=9$, $x=-5$
21. $x=-2$
22. C

Practice 134

a. Not a function
b. Function
c. D
d. C
e. 4,120 full size cars

Problem Set 134

1. True
2. False
3. Function
4. Not a function
5. Function
6. Not a function
7. Function
8. B
9. A
10. 0
11. $\frac{5}{2}$
12. D

13. A
14. C
15. A
16. $x=\frac{9}{4},\ y=\frac{3}{4}$
17. $x=-1,\ y=-5$
18. C
19. E
20. $x=3,\ x=-3$
21. E
22. 540 mezzanine tickets
20. $x=\frac{5}{2},\ x=-\frac{7}{2}$
21. $x=\frac{5}{3},\ x=-1$
22. 352 seconds

Practice 135

a. A
b. 33
c. $x=7.16,\ x=0.84$
d. $x=\frac{7}{4},\ x=-\frac{5}{4}$
e. 252 minutes

Problem Set 135

1. False
2. True
3. Not a function
4. Function
5. B
6. E
7. –4
8. 0
9. 14
10. $x=6,\ x=-3$
11. $x=\frac{1}{8},\ x=0$
12. $x=4.83,\ x=-0.83$
13. $y=-1$
14. $x=-3$
15. 5
16. $\frac{3}{4}$
17. A
18. D
19. $x=3,\ x=1$

CHAPTER 19

Practice 136

a. E

b. $x = \frac{3}{10}, -\frac{11}{30}$

c. Mean = 71.86; Median = 71.5; Mode = 69.2

d. B

e. 7

Problem Set 136

1. True
2. False
3. Not a function
4. Function
5. C
6. B
7. 43
8. 22
9. C
10. A
11. A
12. D
13. $x = 4,\ x = -4$
14. $x = -2$
15. $x = \frac{2}{21},\ x = -\frac{4}{21}$
16. A
17. B
18. Mean = 81; Median = 82; Mode = 90
19. Mean = 44.95; Median = 44.5; Mode = 50.6
20. B
21. C
22. 5

Practice 137

a. $x = -2$

b. D

c. Mean = 24.1; Range = 24.6

d. Range = 62; Below the median

e. $7,000

Problem Set 137

1. True
2. True
3. A
4. B
5. E
6. A
7. –3
8. –9
9. $-\frac{11}{4}$
10. $x = 7$
11. $x = -4$
12. E
13. B
14. A
15. D
16. Median = 17.3; Mode = 17.3
17. Mean = 16.8; Range = 12.7
18. A
19. B
20. Median = 49; 25
21. Range = 62; Below the median
22. $54,000

Practice 138

a. Mean = 16.425 seconds; Range = 11.8 seconds

b. Range = 67.8; Above the median

c. 6 people

d. Median = 68; Range = 70

e. 2.5 hours

Problem Set 138

1. True
2. False
3. 13
4. 36
5. $\frac{2}{7}$
6. D
7. E
8. $x = -4$
9. $x = -\frac{9}{2}$
10. $x = 6$
11. $x = -\frac{1}{3}$
12. A
13. A
14. Median = 17.4; Mode = 17.5
15. Mean = 17.25; Range = 11.7
16. Median = 29.5; 53.8
17. Range = 68.5; Above the median
18. 4 people
19. 18 people
20. 5; Mode = 52
21. Median = 55.5; Range = 80
22. 4.5 hours

Practice 139

a. C

b. Median = 5.3; Range = 6.8

c. $\frac{3}{7}$

d. $\frac{1}{16}$

e. 12 quarters

Problem Set 139

1. True
2. True
3. D
4. C
5. A
6. E
7. $x=4$
8. $x=\frac{11}{4}$
9. C
10. D
11. C
12. B
13. Median = 62.7; 42.1
14. Range = 54.9; Below the median
15. 5 students
16. 20 students
17. 3; Mode = 6.2
18. Median = 4.5; Range = 7.8
19. $\frac{3}{5}$
20. $\frac{1}{6}$
21. $\frac{1}{16}$
22. 17 quarters

Practice 140

a. A

b. $\frac{9}{4}$

c. $\frac{1}{4}$

d. 0.4

e. $70,000

Problem Set 140

1. True
2. False
3. B
4. E
5. −13
6. $\frac{16}{9}$
7. D
8. C
9. $x=0,\ x=-7$
10. $x=-4,\ x=-5$
11. Slope = $\frac{1}{3}$; y-intercept = $(0,4)$
12. Slope = 2; y-intercept = $(0,5)$
13. Median = 5.25 hours
14. Mean = 5.5 hours; Range = 7.9 hours
15. 4; Mode = 6.3
16. Median = 6.3; Range = 8.3
17. $\frac{1}{36}$
18. 64 outcomes
19. $\frac{1}{32}$
20. $\frac{1}{3}$
21. $\frac{3}{10}$
22. $224

CHAPTER 20

Practice 141

a. $x = -\frac{1}{2}$
b. B
c. B
d. $\frac{1}{10}$
e. 240 ounces

Problem Set 141

1. True
2. True
3. E
4. B
5. No
6. Yes
7. $x = \frac{1}{2}$
8. $x = -\frac{1}{4}$
9. D
10. C
11. $x = -12, 12$
12. $x = \frac{2}{3}, \frac{4}{3}$
13. C
14. E
15. Median = 45.5; Least value = 34.7, Greatest value = 63.6
16. Range = 71.9; Above the median
17. 5; Mode = 49
18. Median = 50.5; Range = 88
19. $\frac{1}{16}$
20. 40%
21. $\frac{5}{28}$
22. 88 ounces

Practice 142

a. E
b. C
c. $y = 238$
d. $\frac{5}{18}$
e. 7 years old

Problem Set 142

1. False
2. True
3. $E = 35$
4. D
5. $x = -3$
6. $x = -\frac{20}{3}$
7. D
8. A
9. $x = \frac{3}{2}, y = \frac{13}{2}$
10. $x = -1,\ y = 3$
11. B
12. A
13. D
14. B
15. $y = 299$
16. $y = 405$
17. 12 people
18. 12 people
19. $\frac{1}{1{,}296}$
20. 0.3
21. $\frac{1}{4}$
22. 9 years old

CHAPTER TESTS

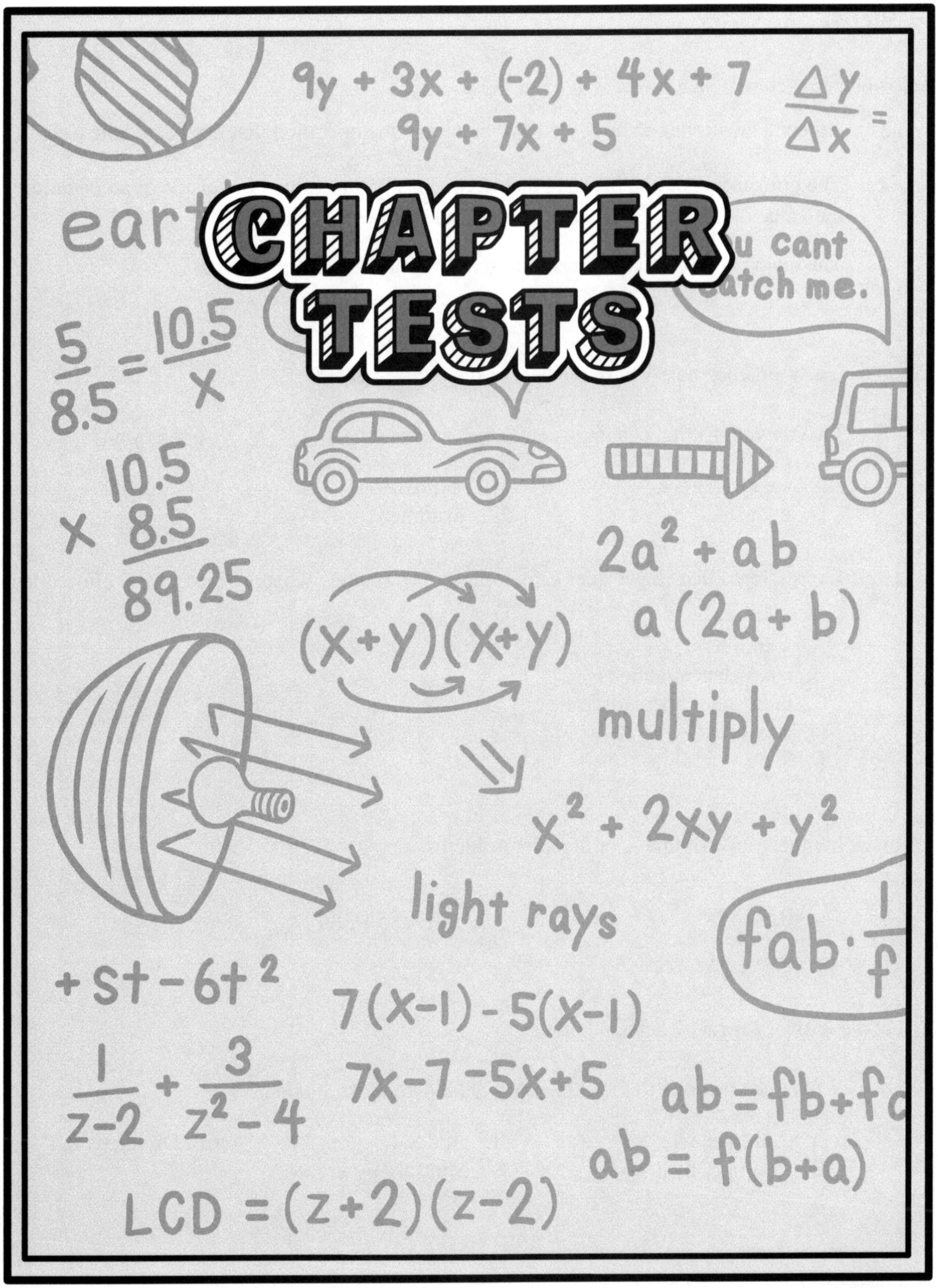

Chapter 1 Test

Tell whether each sentence below is True or False.

1. (3) Algebra equations can be solved by "undoing" the operation that has been done to x.

2. (3) The golden rule of algebra says that if you change the value of one side of an equation the value of the other side must be changed by the same amount.

3. (2) The main purpose of algebra is to find answers to real-life problems.

Complete each sentence below with the best of the choices given.

4. (3) Two operations that can undo each other are called ____________ operations.

A. solution
B. expression
C. algebra
D. inverse
E. arithmetic

5. (5) Expressions that have the same value no matter what x represents are called ____________.

A. solutions
B. equivalent equations
C. equivalent expressions
D. products
E. sums

Tell whether these are arithmetic or algebra problems.

6. (1) $\frac{x}{2}=101$

7. (1) $x=85+384$

Select the answer for each question below.

8. (4) What must be done to the expression $x \div 8.4$ to make it equal x?

A. Subtract 8.4
B. Add 8.4
C. Divide by 8.4
D. Multiply by 8.4
E. Multiply by x

9. **(6)** Which is the algebra way to write the equation $x\times\frac{2}{3}=\frac{1}{4}$?

A. $x=\frac{2}{3}\cdot\frac{1}{4}$ B. $\frac{x}{\frac{2}{3}}=\frac{1}{4}$ C. $\frac{2}{3}x=\frac{1}{4}$

D. $\frac{1}{4}x=\frac{2}{3}$ E. No change is needed.

Answer each question below.

10. **(7)** Write 32.5 % as a decimal.

11. **(8)** Write $\frac{19}{100}$ as a percent.

12. **(9)** The front porch is 216 inches long. How many feet is this?

Tell whether each pair of expressions below is equivalent.

13. **(5)** $\frac{1}{5}-x$ and $x-\frac{1}{5}$

14. **(6)** $5\cdot\frac{x}{5}$ and x

15. **(6)** $\frac{x}{7}$ and $\frac{7}{x}$

Solve each equation below by undoing. Make sure your answers are fully reduced.

16. **(3)** $x+5=24$

17. **(3)** $y-\frac{7}{8}=\frac{3}{4}$

18. **(6)** $68z=306$

19. **(6)** $\frac{x}{11.2}=17$

20. **(3)** $2.1+x=4.5$

21. **(6)** $\frac{1}{7}x=41$

22. **(6)** $\frac{x}{\frac{3}{5}}=\frac{10}{9}$

23. **(6)** $\frac{1}{2}x=\frac{2}{15}$

24. **(3)** $\frac{3}{7}+y=\frac{9}{14}$

Translate the word problem below into an equation; then solve.

25. **(9)** The Henderson family took a trip from Atlanta to Dallas, which are 782 miles apart. If they drove an average speed of 68 mph, how many hours did the trip take?

Chapter 2 Test

Tell whether each sentence below is True or False.

1. (11) The positive and negative whole numbers and zero are all called integers.

2. (11) Opposites are always the same distance from 0 on the number line.

Complete each sentence below with the best of the choices given.

3. (15) If two numbers have the same sign, their product is always ____________.

A. positive
B. negative
C. zero
D. less than 1
E. none of the above

4. (16) If two numbers have different signs, their quotient is always ____________.

A. positive
B. negative
C. zero
D. greater than 1
E. none of the above

For each of the pairs below, indicate which number is greater. (Use a number line if necessary.)

5. (11) -11 or 10

6. (11) $-\frac{5}{6}$ or $-\frac{3}{4}$

Do each calculation below. Make sure your answers are fully reduced.

7. (13) $-18+(-25)$

8. (14) $-6.4-(-7.9)$

9. (15) $(12)(-3)$

10. (13) $\frac{7}{9}+\left(-\frac{7}{9}\right)$

11. (15) $(-40)(-5)$

12. (16) $\frac{28}{-14}$

13. (16) $\frac{-56}{-7}$

14. (15) $\left(-\frac{2}{3}\right)(6)$

15. (16) $\frac{0}{11}$

Tell whether each pair of expressions below is equivalent.

16. (12) $\frac{2}{-5}$ and $\frac{-2}{5}$

17. (11) $9-x$ and $-x+9$

18. (14) $x-\left(-\frac{1}{3}\right)$ and $x-\frac{1}{3}$

Solve each equation below. Make sure your answers are fully reduced.

19. (19) $15-x=37$

20. (17) $x+\left(-\frac{1}{5}\right)=\frac{3}{5}$

21. (17) $\frac{x}{-18.1}=-9.4$

22. (17) $x-(-42)=-51$

23. (19) $-\frac{5}{8}x=20$

24. (19) $\frac{-x}{24}=-4$

Translate the word problem below into an equation; then solve.

25. (7) Mr. Jamison wants to borrow \$375,000 to open a Pizza Shack franchise. If he can pay \$28,125 a year in interest, what interest rate can he afford to pay on his loan? (Write your answer as a percent.)

Chapter 3 Test

Tell whether each sentence below is True or False.

1. (22) In the expression $5(x-9)$, x is multiplied by 5 first and 9 is subtracted second.

2. (23) When solving an equation with more than one operation, the operations should be undone in reverse order.

Complete each sentence below with the best of the choices given.

3. (20) The first order of operations rule states: All ____________ are done first, starting from the left and working to the right.

A. additions
B. subtractions
C. multiplications
D. divisions
E. both C and D

4. (20) The second order of operations rule states: All ____________ are done second, again from left to right.

A. additions
B. subtractions
C. multiplications
D. divisions
E. both A and B

5. (20) The third order of operations rule states: If a different order is needed, the operations that are supposed to be first must be ____________or____________.

A. underlined; crossed out
B. enclosed in parentheses; put inside a fraction
C. highlighted; circled
D. either A or C
E. none of the above

Calculate the value of each expression below.

6. (25) $7(3)+\frac{6}{2}-9$

7. (25) $2(9-3)+\frac{6+4}{5}$

Select the correct mathematical expression for each of the following phrases.

8. (20) 8 and 2 multiplied, and 4 added to that total

A. $8 \cdot 2+4$
B. $8+2 \cdot 4$
C. $8 \cdot 2 \cdot 4$
D. $(8+2)4$
E. $8(2+4)$

9. The quantity $7-13$, all multiplied by 2
(20)

A. $7-13(2)$ B. $7(2)-13$ C. $7\cdot 13-2$
D. $(2-7)\cdot 13$ E. $2(7-13)$

10. The sum of 9 and 15, divided by the sum of -5 and 1
(22)

A. $9+15+\dfrac{-5}{1}$ B. $\dfrac{9+15}{-5}+1$ C. $\dfrac{-5+1}{9+15}$
D. $\dfrac{9+15}{-5+1}$ E. $9+15\div -5+1$

Select the order in which the operations should be performed on x in each equation below.

11. $\dfrac{x}{2}+18=39$
(22)

A. Divide x by 2 first, then add 18 to that total second.
B. Add 18 to x first, then divide that total by 2 second.
C. Add 18 to 2 first, then divide that total into x second.

12. $-21(x+3)=102$
(21)

A. Do x minus 21 first, then multiply that total by 3 second.
B. Add 3 to x first, then multiply that total by -21 second.
C. Multiply -21 and x first, then add 3 to that total second.

13. $\dfrac{x-14}{7}=25$
(22)

A. Subtract 7 from 14 first, then divide that total into x second.
B. Divide 14 by 7 first, then subtract that total from x second.
C. Subtract 14 from x first, then divide that result by 7 second.

Tell whether each of the following pairs of expressions is equivalent.

14. $5+9(x-6)-13$ and $14(x-6)-13$
(26)

15. $(-6)(2x)(-4)$ and $48x$
(27)

Select the simplified form of each expression below.

16. $32+11x-29$
(26)

A. $14x$ B. $43x-29$ C. $32-18x$
D. $11x+3$ E. $11x+61$

17. $(-10)\left(\frac{1}{2}x\right)(4)$
(27)

A. $-14\frac{1}{2}x$ B. $-\frac{10}{8}x$ C. $20x$
D. $-20x$ E. $\frac{4}{20}x$

18. $-7+\frac{x+1}{2}-15$
(27)

A. $\frac{x+1}{2}+105$ B. $\frac{x+1}{2}-22$ C. $\frac{x+1}{2}+8$
D. $-\frac{x+1}{2}-105$ E. $-7+\frac{x-14}{2}$

Solve each equation below. (Remember to undo in reverse order.)

19. $3x+9=30$
(23)

20. $-5(x+6)=15$
(23)

21. $3+\frac{x}{4}-1=-7$
(26)

22. $\frac{1}{3}(-12x)=-24$
(27)

23. $5-4(2-x)=17$
(25)

24. $19+\frac{x+3}{2}-14=1$
(27)

Translate the word problem below into an equation; then solve.

25. Steve gave away half of the stamps in his stamp collection to his best friend, Brad. Then Steve gave away 27 stamps to his sister, Kara. If Steve now has just 15 stamps left, how many stamps were in his collection originally?
(22)

Chapter 4 Test

Tell whether each sentence below is True or False.

1. The number multiplied by x (or any other letter) is called a coefficient.
(28)

2. The quick way to combine two x terms is to add their coefficients.
(28)

Calculate the value of each expression below.

3. $3(7+2)-5(-2)$
(25)

4. $\frac{18-(-4)}{2}+(-6)(3)$
(25)

Select the simplified form of each expression below.

5. $9x+(-4x)$
(28)

A. $-5x$ B. $5+x$ C. $-\frac{1}{36}x$

D. $-36x$ E. $5x$

6. $x+19x+21$
(30)

A. $x+40$ B. $41x$ C. $1+40x$

D. $20x+21$ E. $20x-21$

7. $-11.4y-3.2y$
(28)

A. $-8.2y$ B. $46.48y$ C. $-43.4y$

D. $14.6y$ E. $-14.6y$

8. $\frac{1}{4}z+\frac{1}{5}z$
(28)

A. $\frac{20}{9}z$ B. $\frac{2}{9}z$ C. $\frac{9}{20}z$

D. $\frac{1}{20}z$ E. $9z$

9. (27) $(-2)(-6x)(7)$

A. $84x$ B. $-2+x$ C. $-84x$
D. $-x$ E. $12x+7$

10. (30) $9+2.5x-13+(-x)$

A. $2.5x+22$ B. $-1.5x+4$ C. $3.5x-4$
D. $-2.6x-117$ E. $1.5x+(-4)$

Tell whether each pair of expressions below is equivalent.

11. (26) $-2-6(x+4)-10$ and $-8(x+4)-10$

12. (28) $-x$ and $-19x+18x$

Answer each question below.

13. (29) Jeb can wash a windshield in 12 minutes. Find Jeb's rate per minute for washing windshields.

14. (29) Mrs. Henson, of the Antique Attic, can polish 11 antique chairs in 3 hours. Find Mrs. Henson's rate per hour. (Write your answer as a fraction.)

Solve each equation below.

15. (28) $7x+4x=154$

16. (28) $-3x-5x=72$

17. (26) $3(x-7)+5=32$

18. (28) $-\frac{2}{3}x+\frac{1}{3}+x=\frac{2}{5}$

19. (28) $-5.1y+7.2y=-8.4$

20. (25) $11+\frac{6-x}{2}=26$

21. (30) $-x-\frac{1}{2}x=9$

22. (26) $3+\frac{x}{5}+16=22$

23. (28) $-0.05z+0.9z=51$

Translate the word problem below into an equation; then solve.

24. (31) Two brothers, Bill and Eric, are 4 years apart, and Bill is the older of the two. If the sum of the boys' ages is 28, how old is Bill and how old is Eric?

Chapter 5 Test

Tell whether each sentence below is True or False.

1. (33) An x that's trapped inside parentheses can be "freed" by distributing.

2. (37) In an equation, when freeing an x from within more than one set of parentheses, the innermost parentheses should be distributed over first.

3. (38) Division can be turned into a multiplication by taking the reciprocal of the bottom number (divisor) and multiplying it by the top number.

Calculate the value of each expression below.

4. (37) $-7[4(9-1)]$

5. (37) $3[2+5(6-7)]$

6. (37) $-2\{1-4[8+(-5)]\}$

Free each x (or y) below by rewriting division as multiplication. Make sure your answer is fully simplified then select the best possible choice.

7. (38) $\frac{x}{5}$

A. $\frac{1}{5}x$

B. $\frac{1}{x5}$

C. $\frac{1}{5x}$

D. $\frac{1}{5+x}$

E. $\frac{1}{5}\cdot\frac{1}{x}$

8. (39) $\frac{3x}{8}$

A. $\frac{3}{8x}$

B. $\frac{3}{8+x}$

C. $\frac{3}{8}x$

D. $\frac{3}{x8}$

E. $\frac{3}{8}\cdot\frac{1}{x}$

9. (39) $\frac{y-9}{2}$

A. $\frac{1}{2}y-9$

B. $y-\frac{9}{2}$

C. $\frac{1}{2}y-\frac{9}{2}$

D. $2y-\frac{9}{2}$

E. $-\frac{9}{2}y$

Select the simplified form of each expression below.

10. $11(x-7)$
(34)

A. $11x+77$ B. $11x-7$ C. $11x-77$
D. $-77x$ E. $x-77$

11. $\frac{x}{7}+\frac{4x}{7}$
(39)

A. $\frac{5}{14}x$ B. $\frac{7}{5}x$ C. $\frac{4}{49}x$
D. $\frac{5}{7x}$ E. $\frac{5}{7}x$

12. $\frac{1}{3}(x-3)+\frac{2}{3}(x+3)$
(34)

A. x B. $x+1$ C. $\frac{2}{9}x$
D. $x+\frac{2}{9}$ E. $3x+1$

13. $13x-[9+2(x+4)]$
(37)

A. $2x-4$ B. $6x+8$ C. $11x-13$
D. $11x+17$ E. $11x-17$

14. $\frac{x}{2}-3x+4(x+1)$
(38)

A. $\frac{3}{2}x+4$ B. $7\frac{1}{2}x+4$ C. $\frac{3}{2}x+1$
D. $-6x+1$ E. $\frac{5}{2}x+4$

Tell whether each pair of expressions below is equivalent.

15. $-(x+9)$ and $-x+9$
(35)

16. $\frac{1}{2}x+\frac{x-7}{2}$ and $x-\frac{7}{2}$
(39)

Solve each equation below.

17. (33) $3(x+5)+7x=35$

18. (38) $4x-\frac{x}{2}-3=\frac{1}{2}$

19. (35) $7(x-11)-3x=-53$

20. (35) $-\frac{2}{3}(x-3)-x=8$

21. (39) $\frac{9x}{5}+2x=1$

22. (35) $5x-(12+x)=-13$

23. (39) $2x+\frac{1-x}{4}=3$

24. (37) $4[2(x+3)+7]-5x=61$

Translate the word problem below into an equation; then solve.

25. (36) Brian and Jake left their homes, which are 500 miles apart, and drove straight toward each other. It took 4 hours for the two to meet. If Jake's speed was 15 mph slower than Brian's speed, what was Brian's speed?

Chapter 6 Test

Tell whether each sentence below is True or False.

1. (40) To solve an equation with x terms on both sides, we "move" all the x terms to the same side of the equation.

2. (45) A shortcut for moving a term from one side of an equation to another is to "change its side and change its sign."

3. (46) Every equation has a solution.

Calculate the value of each expression below.

4. (25) $3\left(-\frac{2}{3}+\frac{4}{9}\right)$

5. (25) $(7)(-4)+\frac{3(11-15)}{-2}$

6. (37) $9[5-2(1+4)]$

Select the simplified form of each expression below.

7. (28) $-21+(-20x)+4+34x$

A. $-14x-17$ B. $-21+18x$ C. $14x+27$
D. $54x-17$ E. $14x+(-17)$

8. (39) $\frac{z}{5}-\frac{4z}{5}$

A. $-\frac{3z}{10}$ B. $-\frac{3}{5}z$ C. $-\frac{4}{25}z$
D. $\frac{1}{2}z$ E. z

9. (33) $3(4x+3)+2(7x+1)$

A. $2x+18$ B. $26x+2$ C. $26x+11$
D. $26x+4$ E. $5(11x+4)$

10. **(27)** $(-7)\left(\frac{2}{7}x\right)(-3)$

A. $2x-3$ B. $6x$ C. $\frac{6}{49}x$

D. $-6x$ E. $-10\frac{2}{7}x$

11. **(35)** $4(y+5)-(y-9)$

A. $3y+11$ B. $5y-4$ C. $3y+14$

D. $3(2y-4)$ E. $3y+29$

12. **(37)** $\frac{1}{2}[5(x+2)+4x]$

A. $\frac{13}{2}x+2$ B. $\frac{9}{2}x+1$ C. $14x+27$

D. $\frac{9}{2}x+5$ E. $\frac{19x}{2}$

Tell whether each of the following expressions is equivalent.

13. **(39)** $\frac{x+5}{3}+\frac{1}{3}x$ and $\frac{2}{3}x+\frac{5}{3}$

14. **(35)** $9-2(x+5)$ and $7x+35$

15. **(37)** $9y-[3-8(y-4)]$ and $17y+(-35)$

Solve each equation below. (Indicate any false equations or identities.)

16. **(41)** $8x-13=11+5x$

17. **(28)** $\frac{1}{3}x+\frac{1}{2}x+6=11$

18. **(41)** $7x-9=2x$

19. **(41)** $5(y-3)=2(y+12)$

20. **(45)** $\frac{7}{8}x=\frac{1}{2}$

21. **(41)** $7x+5+1-3x=4x+6$

22. **(37)** $2x-[11(x-4)+3]=77$

23. **(41)** $18-8x=7x-12$

24. **(41)** $-\frac{1}{4}x-4+\frac{3}{4}x=\frac{1}{2}x+1$

Translate the word problem below into an equation; then solve.

25. (29) Chef Charles has already broken 14 eggs, and he's breaking eggs at a rate of 12 per minute. Chef Louis has already broken 22 eggs, and he's breaking eggs at a rate of 10 per minute. How many minutes will it take for Charles to have broken as many eggs as Louis?

Chapter 7 Test

Tell whether each sentence below is True or False.

1. (47) According to the law of equivalent fractions, the numerator and denominator of a fraction can be multiplied or divided by the same number without changing the fraction's value.

2. (47) Rewriting a number or expression as a multiplication is called "factoring."

3. (48) Canceling is just a shortcut for dividing the top and bottom of a fraction by the number being canceled.

Select the factored form of each expression below.

4. (51) $3x-27$

A. $9(3x-2)$ B. $3(x-9)$ C. $27(9x-1)$
D. $3(x-24)$ E. Not factorable

5. (51) $7x+45$

A. $7(x+38)$ B. $45(5x+1)$ C. $7(x+5)$
D. $7(x+8)$ E. Not factorable

6. (52) $-28-42x$

A. $-14(2-3x)$ B. $-7(4+7x)$ C. $-14(2+3x)$
D. $-14(3+2x)$ E. Not factorable

Select the simplified form of each expression below.

7. (37) $5[7x-8(1+x)]$

A. $13x+(-8)$ B. $-5x+(-40)$ C. $75x-40$
D. $40x+(-40)$ E. $27x-8$

8. (35) $0.25(3x-2)-2.5(2x+4)$

A. $-4.25x+2$ B. $-1.25x+2$ C. $-2.25(5x+2)$
D. $-4.25x+9.5$ E. $-4.25x+(-10.5)$

Select the fully reduced form of each fraction below.

9. **(52)** $\dfrac{5(z+4)}{8z+32}$

A. $\dfrac{8}{5}$ B. $\dfrac{5z}{8z+8}$ C. $-3z+(-12)$

D. $40z+160$ E. $\dfrac{5}{8}$

10. **(52)** $\dfrac{21x+7}{6x+2}$

A. $14(3x+1)$ B. $42x+14$ C. $\dfrac{2}{7}$

D. $15x+5$ E. $\dfrac{7}{2}$

11. **(52)** $\dfrac{-9x}{15x-6}$

A. $\dfrac{-6x}{5x-2}$ B. $-\dfrac{x}{15x-6}$ C. $\dfrac{1}{6x-6}$

D. $-\dfrac{3x}{5x-2}$ E. $-\dfrac{27x}{5x-2}$

Multiply or divide (as indicated) the fractions and select the simplified answer below.

12. **(53)** $\dfrac{11}{10x}\cdot\dfrac{5x}{22}$

A. $\dfrac{1}{4}$ B. $\dfrac{1}{2}$ C. 4

D. $\dfrac{1}{4x}$ E. $\dfrac{11+5x}{10x+22}$

13. **(54)** $\dfrac{x-3}{15}\div\dfrac{6x-18}{5x}$

A. 1 B. $\dfrac{x}{9}$ C. $\dfrac{x}{18}$

D. $\dfrac{7x-21}{20x}$ E. $\dfrac{x-1}{6x-18}$

14. (53) $\frac{3y-12}{28}\cdot\frac{14y+7}{6y-24}$

A. $16y+8$

B. $\frac{2y+1}{8}$

C. $\frac{17y-5}{6y+4}$

D. $\frac{2y+1}{2}$

E. $\frac{2y+1}{6}$

Add or subtract (as indicated) the fractions and select the simplified answer below.

15. (55) $\frac{7}{9x}+\frac{2}{x}$

A. $\frac{9}{10x}$

B. $\frac{7+18x}{9x}$

C. $\frac{14}{9x}$

D. $\frac{25x}{9}$

E. $\frac{25}{9x}$

16. (56) $\frac{x+4}{2x}-\frac{2x+1}{6x}$

A. $-\frac{3}{2x}$

B. $\frac{x+13}{6x}$

C. $\frac{x+3}{6x}$

D. $\frac{x+11}{6x}$

E. $\frac{3x-3}{4x}$

17. (55) $\frac{1}{x+5}+\frac{2}{2x+10}$

A. $\frac{1}{3x+10}$

B. $\frac{2}{x+5}$

C. $\frac{1}{2x+15}$

D. $\frac{1}{x+5}$

E. 1

Tell whether each pair of expressions below is equivalent.

18. (35) $-24x+(-18)$ and $-6(4x+3)$

19. (39) $\frac{9x+5}{5}$ and $9x$

Solve each equation below.

20. (41) $6+4x+3=6x-21$

21. (41) $4(x-5)=7(x+2)$

22. (39) $\frac{5(x-8)}{6}=-7$

23. (28) $\frac{3}{4}x+\frac{1}{4}x=19$

24. (37) $5y-[2(y+1)+2]=7y$

Translate the word problem below into an equation; then solve.

25. (44) Professor Baird wants to mix a solution containing 10% acid with one containing 15% acid to obtain a 20-ounce solution containing 12% acid. How many ounces of the 10% solution should the professor use?

Chapter 8 Test

Tell whether each sentence below is True or False.

1. (62) To eliminate or "clear" the fractions from an equation, you multiply both sides of the equation by the lowest common denominator (LCD) of the fractions.

2. (62) The LCD must have all the factors that appear in each denominator, but no extra factors at all.

Answer each question below.

3. (59) Write the ratio 9 : 13 as a fraction.

4. (59) Write the fraction $\frac{3}{15}$ as a ratio with a colon.

Select the fully reduced form of each fraction below.

5. (51) $\dfrac{25x+10}{5x}$

A. $\dfrac{5x+2}{x}$ B. $25x+2$ C. $20x+10$

D. $5x+10$ E. 7

6. (52) $\dfrac{18x}{6-12x}$

A. $6+6x$ B. $3x-\dfrac{3}{2}$ C. $\dfrac{3x}{1-2x}$

D. $\dfrac{3x}{1-12x}$ E. -3

7. (52) $\dfrac{15y+5}{-21y-7}$

A. $36y+12$ B. $\dfrac{5(3y+1)}{-7(3y-1)}$ C. $-6y+(-2)$

D. $-\dfrac{5}{7}$ E. -35

Multiply or divide (as indicated) the fractions and select the simplified answer below.

8. (53) $\frac{5x-10}{6}\cdot\frac{12}{3x-6}$

A. $\frac{17}{9}$ B. $\frac{10}{3}$ C. 30

D. $\frac{5x+2}{3x}$ E. $\frac{5}{24}$

9. (54) $\frac{14x+7}{x}\div\frac{21}{2x}$

A. $\frac{2x+1}{3}$ B. $\frac{14x+28}{3x}$ C. $\frac{16x+7}{x+21}$

D. $\frac{294x+147}{2x}$ E. $\frac{4x+2}{3}$

10. (53) $\frac{20-25x}{15}\cdot\frac{3x+9}{8-10x}$

A. $\frac{x+3}{2}$ B. $\frac{29-22x}{23-10x}$ C. $\frac{3x+9}{2}$

D. $\frac{2}{9x+27}$ E. $\frac{1}{2}$

Add or subtract (as indicated) the fractions and select the simplified answer below.

11. (55) $\frac{5x}{4x-8}+\frac{x+2}{x-2}$

A. $\frac{4x-2}{3x-6}$ B. $\frac{5x}{4x+8}$ C. $\frac{6x+2}{5x-10}$

D. $\frac{9x+2}{4x-8}$ E. $\frac{9x+8}{4x-8}$

12. (56) $\frac{9}{2(x+3)}-\frac{x}{x+3}$

A. $\frac{9+x}{3x+9}$ B. $\frac{9-x}{2x+6}$ C. $\frac{7}{2x+6}$

D. $\frac{9-2x}{2x+6}$ E. $\frac{9}{2x}$

13. $\dfrac{x}{3x+12}-\dfrac{x+1}{x+4}$
(56)

A. $\dfrac{2x+1}{4x+16}$ B. $\dfrac{x}{3x+3}$ C. $\dfrac{-2x+(-3)}{3x+12}$

D. $\dfrac{-2x+3}{3x+12}$ E. $-\dfrac{1}{3x+12}$

Find the LCD of each group of fractions below.

14. $\dfrac{2}{5}, \dfrac{11}{9y}$
(62)

15. $\dfrac{1}{3x}, \dfrac{2}{x}, \dfrac{3}{7}$
(62)

16. Select the LCD of the group of fractions $\dfrac{5}{2(x+1)}, \dfrac{9}{2x}, \dfrac{1}{4}$.
(62)

A. $4x$ B. $4(x+1)$ C. $2x(x+1)$

D. $4x(x+1)$ E. $2(x+1)$

Tell whether each pair of expressions below is equivalent.

17. $3[7-2(x+4)]$ and $-6x+(-3)$
(37)

18. $\dfrac{5y-8}{8-5y}$ and -1
(51)

Solve each equation below. (Make sure your solutions do not require division by zero.)

19. $\dfrac{5.4}{2y}=9$
(58)

20. $\dfrac{7}{4x+3}=2$
(58)

21. $1-\dfrac{3}{5x}=\dfrac{4}{10x}$
(61)

22. $\dfrac{3z}{2}+\dfrac{1}{4}=\dfrac{7}{8}$
(24)

23. $9x=7(x-2)$
(41)

24. $\dfrac{4}{3(x+2)}-\dfrac{2}{3x}=\dfrac{1}{x+2}$
(41)

Translate the word problem below into an equation; then solve.

25. The ratio of golf balls to tennis balls in the pro shop is 5 : 4. If there are 385 golf balls, how many tennis balls are there?
(59)

Chapter 9 Test

Tell whether each sentence below is True or False.

1. A power is a short way of writing a repeated multiplication.
(64)

2. All exponents must be greater than 1.
(70)

Calculate the value of each expression below.

3. $8-(7-3)^2$
(64)

4. $\dfrac{22-4^2}{3}+2^3$
(64)

Rewrite each number below in scientific notation.

5. 11,400,000,000,000
(65)

6. 0.0000000054
(71)

Simplify each expression below. (Leave your answer in scientific notation.)

7. $(1.4\times10^6)(3.2\times10^4)$
(71)

8. $\dfrac{2.5\times10^3}{5\times10^8}$
(71)

Find the area of the square and the volume of the cube below.

9.
(64)

10.
(64)

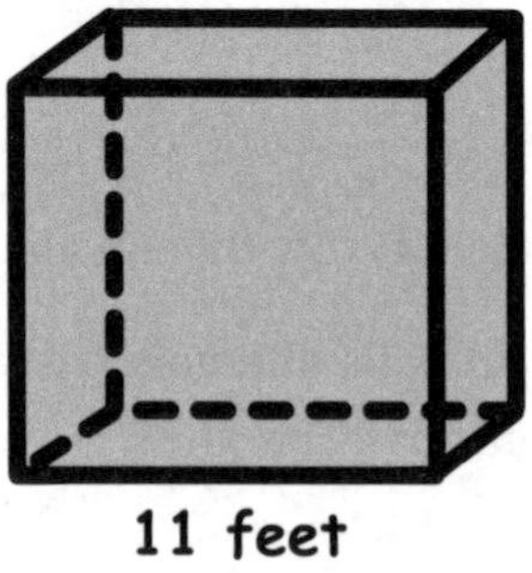

Select the simplified form of each expression below.

11. $9x^3+2x^2+5x^3+4x^2$
(67)

A. $45x^3+8x^2$ B. $20x^{10}$ C. $14x^3+6x^2$
D. $14x^6+6x^4$ E. $45x^6+8x^4$

12. $(3y^2)(5y^7)(2y^4)$
(68)

A. $30y^{56}$ B. $10y^{56}$ C. $10y^{13}$
D. $20y^{15}$ E. $30y^{13}$

Select the fully reduced form of each fraction below

13. $\dfrac{9x^3}{15x^7}$
(70)

A. $\dfrac{3}{5x^4}$ B. $\dfrac{3}{5x^{10}}$ C. $\dfrac{1}{6x^4}$
D. $\dfrac{x^4}{24}$ E. $\dfrac{3x^4}{5}$

14. $\dfrac{5y^2+10y}{6y^4+12y^3}$
(72)

A. $\dfrac{3y^2}{5}$ B. $\dfrac{y+2}{6y^2}$ C. $\dfrac{5}{6y}$
D. $\dfrac{5}{6y^2}$ E. $\dfrac{5y}{6}$

Multiply or divide (as indicated) the fractions and select the simplified answer below.

15. $\dfrac{10x^9}{8}\cdot\dfrac{2}{15x^3}$
(73)

A. $\dfrac{75}{8}x^6$ B. $\dfrac{x^3}{6}$ C. $\dfrac{10x^9+2}{8+15x^3}$
D. $\dfrac{5}{30x^6}$ E. $\dfrac{x^6}{6}$

16. $\frac{4}{3x^7} \div \frac{x-2}{9x^5}$
(73)

A. $\frac{12x^5}{x^8 - 2x^7}$ B. $\frac{4x+(-8)}{27x^{12}}$ C. $\frac{12}{x^3 - 2x^2}$

D. $\frac{7}{x^2 + x - 2}$ E. $\frac{2+x}{12x^{12}}$

Distribute in the expressions below and select the simplified answer below.

17. $x(x^2 + 3)$
(72)

A. $x^2 + x + 3$ B. $x^3 + 3$ C. $2x^2 + 3x$

D. $3x+3$ E. $x^3 + 3x$

18. $(x+7)(x+3)$
(69)

A. $x^2 + 10x + 10$ B. $x^2 + 10x + 21$ C. $x^2 + 21$

D. $2x+10$ E. $x^2 + 21x + 21$

19. $(x-2)(x^2 - 2x + 1)$
(69)

A. $x^3 + (-4x^2) + (-x) + 1$ B. $x^3 + 5x + (-2)$ C. $x^3 + (-4x^2) + 5x + (-2)$

D. $x^3 + (-2x^2) + x$ E. $x^2 + (-x) + (-1)$

Add or subtract (as indicated) the fractions and select the simplified answer below.

20. $\frac{1}{5y^4} + \frac{2}{y^3}$
(73)

A. $\frac{1+10y}{5y^4}$ B. $\frac{2}{5y^7}$ C. $\frac{1+2y}{5y^4}$

D. $\frac{1}{10y}$ E. $\frac{3}{5y^4 + y^3}$

21. $\frac{2x+3}{x^4} - \frac{x+2}{x^3}$
(73)

A. $\frac{2x^2 + 7x + 6}{x^7}$ B. $\frac{x+1}{x^4}$ C. $\frac{2x+3}{x^2 + 2x}$

D. $\frac{-x^2 + 3}{x^4}$ E. $\frac{-x^2 + 4x + 3}{x^4}$

Solve each equation below. (Make sure your solutions do not require division by zero.)

22. **(58)** $\dfrac{2x-3}{5x}=\dfrac{11}{2}$

23. **(60)** $\dfrac{4}{z}+\dfrac{1}{z}=\dfrac{2}{z+3}$

24. **(41)** $7(x-2)-5x=-3x$

Translate the word problem below into an equation; then solve.

25. (32) The piggybank had \$25.65 in dimes and quarters. If there were 20 more quarters than dimes, how many dimes were in the piggybank?

Chapter 10 Test

Tell whether each sentence below is True or False.

1. (74) The inverse of raising a number to a power is called taking a "root."

2. (76) An irrational number, such as $\sqrt{2}$, cannot be written exactly as a whole number or fraction.

Calculate the value of each expression below.

3. (74) $\sqrt[4]{16}$

4. (75) $\sqrt{7^2}$

Tell whether each of the roots below is rational or irrational.

5. (76) $\sqrt{17}$

6. (76) $\sqrt[3]{8}$

Tell which of the two numbers in each of the pairs below is greater. (Use estimates for the irrationals.)

7. (76) $\sqrt{23}$ or 4

8. (76) $\sqrt{78}$ or 9

Use a calculator to find decimal estimates to two decimal places (hundredths) for each of the following irrational numbers.

9. (76) $\sqrt{11}$

10. (76) $\sqrt{43}$

Find the length of the missing side for each of the right triangles below. (Estimate an irrational answer to two decimal places.)

11. **(78)**

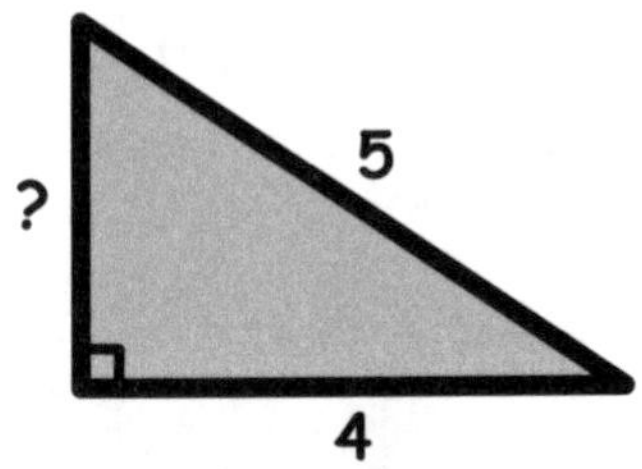

12. **(78)**

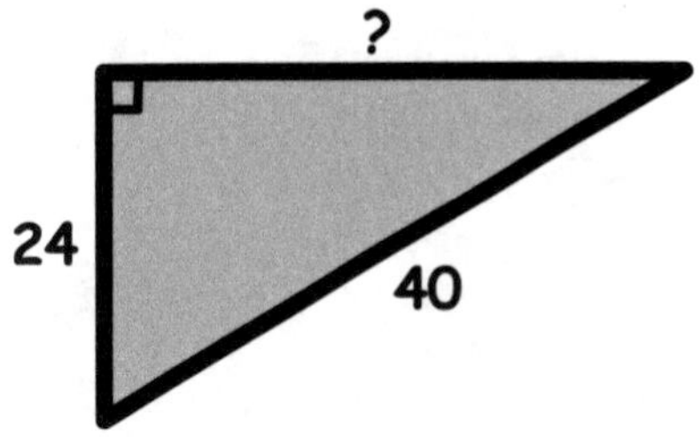

Multiply or divide (as indicated) the fractions and select the simplified answer below.

13. **(73)** $\dfrac{y^3+5y^2}{21y^3}\cdot\dfrac{9y^3}{y+5}$

A. $\dfrac{y^2}{7}$ B. $\dfrac{9y^2}{21}$ C. $\dfrac{3y^2}{7}$

D. $\dfrac{7}{y^2}$ E. $\dfrac{10y^3+5y^2}{21y^3+y+5}$

14. **(54)** $\dfrac{3x}{16}\div\dfrac{3x-9}{20}$

A. $\dfrac{20}{16x-48}$ B. $\dfrac{5x}{4x-3}$ C. $\dfrac{6x-9}{36}$

D. $\dfrac{20x}{4x-3}$ E. $\dfrac{5x}{4x-12}$

Distribute in the expressions and select the simplified answer below.

15. **(69)** $(x^2-5)(x+2)$

A. $x^3+x^2+(-x)+(-3)$ B. $x^2-5x-10$ C. x^3-10

D. $x^3+2x^2+(-5x)+(-10)$ E. $x^3+(-5x^2)+2x+10$

16. **(69)** $3x[x+2(x+4)]$

A. $9x^2+8x$ B. $21x^2$ C. $9x^2+24x$

D. $3x^2+2x+8$ E. $9x^2+12x$

Add or subtract (as indicated) the fractions and select the simplified answer below.

17. (73) $\frac{5x}{7x}+\frac{10x}{x^2}$

A. $\frac{75x}{7x}$ B. $\frac{5x+10}{7x}$ C. $\frac{75}{7x}$

D. $\frac{15x}{7x^2}$ E. $\frac{5x+70}{7x}$

18. (73) $\frac{13}{x+2}-\frac{6}{x^2+2x}$

A. $\frac{6x-13}{x^2+2x}$ B. $\frac{13x-6}{x^2+2x}$ C. $\frac{13x}{6}$

D. $\frac{7}{x^2+2x}$ E. $\frac{78}{x^3+4x^2+4x}$

Tell whether each pair of expressions below is equivalent.

19. (67) $-3x^4+2x^3+9x^4-5x^3$ and $6x^8+(-3x^6)$

20. (68) $(4y^5)(3y^5)$ and $12y^{10}$

Solve each equation below.

21. (41) $7x-3(x+2)=x+5$

22. (76) $\sqrt[3]{x}=3$

23. (61) $\frac{x-1}{2}=\frac{x-9}{11}$

24. (39) $\frac{y+4}{3y-8}=1$

Translate the word problem below into an equation; then solve.

25. (32) Todd is 33 years old; his nephew Jacob is 12. In how many years will Jacob be $\frac{1}{2}$ his uncle Todd's age?

Chapter 11 Test

Tell whether each sentence below is True or False.

1. **(79)** Quadratic (second-degree) equations can have two solutions.

2. **(85)** To find the right number to add when completing the square, take half of the coefficient of the x term and square it.

Select the degree of each equation below.

3. **(79)** $3x^2 + 5x = 2$

A. 1st degree B. 2nd degree C. 3rd degree
D. 4th degree E. 5th degree

4. **(79)** $x^3 - 2x^2 + 4x + 1 = 0$

A. 1st degree B. 2nd degree C. 3rd degree
D. 4th degree E. 5th degree

Answer each question below.

5. **(80)** Which choice below lists *all* of the square roots of the number 81?

A. $3, -3$ B. $\sqrt{3}, -\sqrt{3}$ C. 9
D. -3 E. $9, -9$

6. **(80)** Which choice below lists *all* of the square roots of the number 13?

A. $\sqrt{13}, -\sqrt{13}$ B. $\sqrt{13}$ C. $-\sqrt{13}$
D. $\sqrt{26}, -\sqrt{26}$ E. $+13, -13$

Rewrite each of the numbers below in scientific notation.

7. **(65)** 291,100,000,000

8. **(71)** 0.000000035

Select the factored form of each expression below.

9. $24y^4 - 6y^2$
(72)

A. $6y^2(4y^4 - 1)$ B. $24y^2(y^2 - 1)$ C. $y^2(24y^2 - 6)$
D. $24y(y^3 - y)$ E. $6y^2(4y^2 - 1)$

10. $x^2 - 7x + 12$
(83)

A. $(x-4)(x-3)$ B. $(x+1)(x+12)$ C. $(x+2)(x+6)$
D. $(x-7)(x+12)$ E. $(x+4)(x+3)$

Select the fully simplified expression for the area of each rectangle below.

11.
(79)

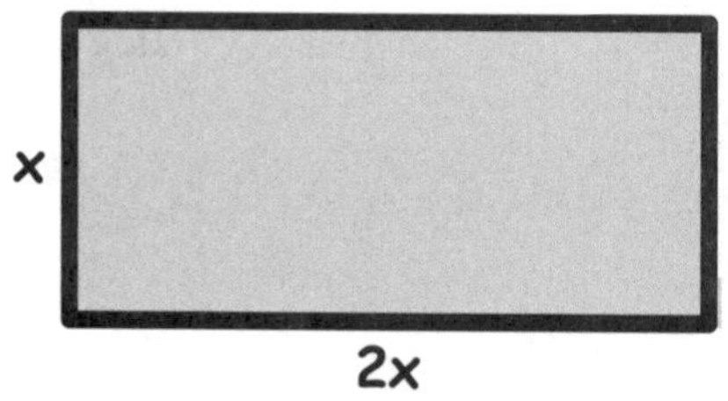

A. $3x$ B. $\frac{1}{2}$ C. $3x^2$
D. $2x$ E. $2x^2$

12.
(79)

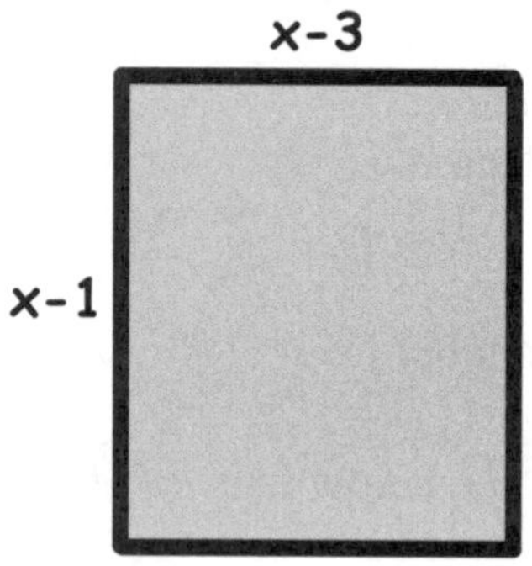

A. $x^2 + 3$ B. $2x - 4$ C. $x^2 + 3x + (-3)$
D. $x^2 + (-4x) + 3$ E. $x^2 + (-2x) + 3$

Select the fully reduced form of each fraction below.

13. $\dfrac{y^2 - 5y}{2y - 10}$
(72)

A. $\dfrac{y}{10}$ B. $\dfrac{1}{y^2 - 3y - 10}$ C. $\dfrac{y}{2}$
D. $\dfrac{2}{y}$ E. $\dfrac{y-5}{2}$

14. $\dfrac{9x^3-27x}{18x^2}$
(72)

A. $\dfrac{x^2-3}{2x}$ B. $\dfrac{x^2}{2}$ C. $\dfrac{x^2-3}{2}$

D. $2x^3-6x$ E. $\dfrac{x^2-3}{9x}$

Multiply or divide (as indicated) the fractions and select the simplified answer below.

15. $\dfrac{\frac{25}{4x}}{\frac{10x^2}{8x^4}}$
(54)

A. $\dfrac{45}{16x^5}$ B. $\dfrac{1}{5x}$ C. $\dfrac{25+8x^4}{4x+10x^2}$

D. $10x$ E. $5x$

16. $\dfrac{y^3-4y}{16y^2}\cdot\dfrac{-8y}{3y^3-12y}$
(73)

A. $-\dfrac{1}{6y}$ B. $\dfrac{y^3-12y}{3y^3+16y^2-12y}$ C. $-\dfrac{8}{19y}$

D. $\dfrac{-7y}{16y^2+3y}$ E. $-\dfrac{y}{3}$

Add or subtract (as indicated) the fractions and select the simplified answer below.

17. $\dfrac{x^2+2}{4}+\dfrac{2x^2-1}{5}$
(55)

A. $\dfrac{5x^2+10}{8x^2-4}$ B. $\dfrac{3x^2+1}{20}$ C. $\dfrac{13x^2+1}{20}$

D. $\dfrac{13x^2+6}{20}$ E. $\dfrac{2x^4+3x^2+(-2)}{20}$

18. $\dfrac{12x^2}{x^2-3}-\dfrac{36}{x^2-3}$
(56)

A. $\dfrac{12x^2+36}{x^2-3}$ B. 24 C. 12

D. $\dfrac{x^2}{3}$ E. $\dfrac{432x^2}{x^2-3}$

Solve each quadratic (second-degree) equation below and select the choice that contains *all* of the solutions.

19. $(x-3)^2+4=20$
(80)

A. $x=11,\ -5$ B. $x=7$ C. $x=11$
D. $x=1,\ -7$ E. $x=7,\ -1$

20. $2x^2+6x^2=40$
(80)

A. $x=\sqrt{2},\ -\sqrt{2}$ B. $x=5,\ -5$ C. $x=10\sqrt{2},\ -10\sqrt{2}$
D. $x=\sqrt{5},\ -\sqrt{5}$ E. $x=20,\ -20$

Solve each quadratic (second-degree) equation below by factoring.

21. $3x^2+9x=0$
(83)

22. $x^2+13x=-12$
(83)

Solve each quadratic (second-degree) equation below by completing the square. (Estimate any irrational answers to two decimal places.)

23. $x^2+4x=2$
(85)

24. $2x^2+8x-1=0$
(85)

Translate the word problem below into an equation; then solve.

25. Mr. Graham invested some of his $18,000 in bonds that made a 5% profit and the rest in bonds that made a 12% profit. If the profit on the 12% bonds was $885 more than the profit on the 5% bonds, how much did Mr. Graham invest in the 5% bonds?
(44)

Chapter 12 Test

Tell whether each sentence below is True or False.

1. (87) A relationship between changing quantities can be shown with a table or an equation.

2. (87) Unknowns that can represent all sorts of numbers are called "variables."

Simplify each expression below. (Leave your answer in scientific notation.)

3. (68) $(2.6\times10^{4})(4.5\times10^{12})$

4. (70) $\dfrac{1.6\times10^{-7}}{3.2\times10^{-11}}$

Distribute in the expressions and select the simplified answer below.

5. (69) $y^2(-3y-7)$

A. y^2-3y-7 B. $21y^3$ C. $-3y^3-7$
D. $-2y^3-7y^2$ E. $-3y^3+(-7y^2)$

6. (69) $(x+4)(x+9)$

A. x^2+36 B. $2x+13$ C. $x^2+36x+13$
D. $x^2+5x+36$ E. $x^2+13x+36$

Tell whether each pair of expressions below is equivalent.

7. (68) $(5y^4)^3$ and $125y^{12}$

8. (68) $(3x^2)(6x^{-4})$ and $\dfrac{18}{x^2}$

For the two-variable equation $y=2x+(-5)$, find the matching y value for each x value below.

9. (87) $x=-2$ $y=?$

10. (87) $x=\dfrac{1}{2}$ $y=?$

Tell whether each of the following pairs of numbers is a solution to the two-variable equation $y-5x=1$.

11. (87) $x=1 \quad y=1$

12. (87) $x=0.2 \quad y=2$

Solve each equation below.

13. (39) $\dfrac{-3(x+2)}{4}=15$

14. (61) $\dfrac{1}{x}-\dfrac{3}{x+2}=\dfrac{3}{x+2}$

Solve each quadratic (second-degree) equation below. (Estimate any irrational answers to two decimal places.)

15. (80) $3x^2+2=50$

16. (80) $3(x+5)^2=21$

Solve each quadratic (second-degree) equation below by factoring.

17. (81) $3x^2+6x=0$

18. (82) $x^2-x-20=0$

Complete the table for each two-variable equation below.

19. (87) $y=4x-1$

x	-2	-1	0	1	2	3
y	-9	-5	-1			

20. (87) $y=11-2x$

x	-2	-1	0	1	2	3
y				9	7	5

Answer each question below.

21. (90) If a bowling ball is dropped out of an airplane, what will its speed (velocity) be after 3.4 seconds, assuming no air resistance? (Hint: Use the equation $v = 32t$.)

22. (90) How long would it take the bowling ball to fall 150 feet? (Estimate your answer to one decimal place. Hint: Use the equation $d = 16t^2$.)

For each problem below, select the choice that represents the two-variable equation after it has been solved for *y* in terms of *x*.

23. (88) $y - 5x = 9$

A. $y = 14x$ B. $y = 45x$ C. $y = -5x + 9$

D. $y = 5x + 9$ E. $y = \frac{9}{5x}$

24. (88) $3(y + 4) = x$

A. $y = \frac{x - 12}{3}$ B. $y = 3x - 4$ C. $y = \frac{x - 4}{3}$

D. $y = \frac{1}{3x - 4}$ E. $y = x^3 - 4$

Translate the word problem below into an equation; then solve.

25. (21) The sum of three consecutive odd integers is 243. What is the *smallest* of these integers?

Chapter 13 Test

Tell whether each sentence below is True or False.

1. (94) Like terms with several variables can be combined by the shortcut of adding or subtracting their coefficients.

2. (99) A difference of two squares such as $a^2 - b^2$ factors into the form $(a + b)(a - b)$.

Select the factored form of each expression below.

3. (99) $x^2 + 2xy + y^2$

A. $(x+y)(x+y)$ B. $(x^2+y^2)(x^2-y^2)$ C. $(x+y)(x-y)$
D. $(x+y)(x+2y)$ E. $(x-y)(x-y)$

4. (100) $4x^2 - 9y^2$

A. $(2x+3y)(2x+3y)$ B. $(4x-9y)(3x+9y)$ C. $(2x-3y)(2x-3y)$
D. $(3x+2y)(3x-2y)$ E. $(2x+3y)(2x-3y)$

Select the fully simplified form of each expression below.

5. (98) $7a^3b^2c + 6a^3b^2c$

A. $42a^9b^4c$ B. $13a^3b^2c$ C. a^3b^2c
D. $42a^3b^2c$ E. $13a^6b^4c^2$

6. (95) $(2x^2y^3z)(-9xy^2z^4)$

A. $11x^3y^5z^5$ B. $-7x^3y^5z^4$ C. $-7xyz^3$
D. $-18x^3y^5z^5$ E. $-18x^2y^6z^4$

Distribute in the expressions and select the simplified answer below.

7. (96) $5x^3y^3(x-y)$

A. $5x^4y^3 - 5x^3y^4$ B. $5x^4y^4$ C. $x+5x^3y^3 - y$
D. $5x^3y^4 - 5x^4y^3$ E. $5x^4y^3 - y$

8. (96) $(2x-3y)(5x+2y)$

A. $10x^2-6y^2$
B. $7x^2-11xy-y^2$
C. $10x^2-11xy-6y^2$
D. $10x^2-60xy-6y^2$
E. $7x-y$

Select the fully reduced form of each fraction below

9. (97) $\dfrac{18x^4y^3z}{24x^2y^4z^2}$

A. $\dfrac{4x^8}{3y^{12}z^2}$
B. $\dfrac{3x^2}{4yz}$
C. $\dfrac{x^2}{6yz}$
D. $\dfrac{3x^2y}{4z}$
E. $\dfrac{3z}{4x^2y}$

10. (99) $\dfrac{x-y}{x^2-2xy+y^2}$

A. $x-y$
B. $x+y$
C. $\dfrac{1}{x+y}$
D. $\dfrac{1}{2(x-y)}$
E. $\dfrac{1}{x-y}$

Add or subtract (as indicated) the fractions and select the simplified answer below.

11. (102) $\dfrac{2}{x^3y^2z}-\dfrac{1}{xy^3z^2}$

A. $\dfrac{3}{x^4y^5z^3}$
B. $\dfrac{2z-1}{x^3y^3z^2}$
C. $-\dfrac{2}{x^4y^5z^3}$
D. $\dfrac{2yz-x^2}{x^3y^3z^2}$
E. $\dfrac{1}{x^2yz}$

12. (102) $\dfrac{a}{a-b}-\dfrac{2ab}{a^2-b^2}$

A. $\dfrac{a}{a+b}$
B. $\dfrac{b}{a-b}$
C. $\dfrac{a-2ab}{a^2-b^2}$
D. $\dfrac{2a^2b}{a^2-b^2}$
E. $\dfrac{a^2}{a^2-b^2}$

Tell whether each pair of expressions below is equivalent.

13. **(94)** $-\frac{1}{2}s^2t^5 - \frac{1}{2}s^2t^5$ and $-s^2t^5$

14. **(96)** $(x-y)^2$ and $x^2 - y^2$

Solve each equation below.

15. **(41)** $\frac{7x}{3} - 1 = 2x$

16. **(60)** $\frac{1}{x+2} = \frac{4}{x+3}$

Solve each quadratic (second-degree) equation below by factoring.

17. **(81)** $x^2 = 9x$

18. **(82)** $x^2 - 8x = -12$

Complete the table for the two-variable and three-variable equations below.

19. **(87)** $3y - 2x = 1$

x	-2	-1	0	1	2	3
y		$-\frac{1}{3}$	$\frac{1}{3}$		$\frac{5}{3}$	

20. **(92)** $z = 3xy$

x	-2	-1	0	1	2	3
y	3	4	5	6	7	8
z	-18	-12				72

Answer each question below.

21. **(92)** In the equation $z = 3x^2 + y$, find the value of z when $x = 2$ and $y = -4$.

22. **(92)** In the equation $A = qr^2s$, find the value of A when $q = 3$, $r = -2$, and $s = -1$.

Answer each question below.

23. Which choice below represents the equation $Q = \frac{1}{3}kn^2$ after it has been solved for k?
(103)

A. $k = \frac{1}{3}Qn^2$ B. $k = \frac{Q}{3n^2}$ C. $k = \sqrt{\frac{3Q}{n}}$

D. $k = \frac{3Q}{n^2}$ E. $k = Q - \frac{1}{3}n^2$

24. Which choice below represents the equation $P = \frac{KT}{R}$ after it has been solved for R?
(103)

A. $R = \frac{P}{KT}$ B. $R = KT - P$ C. $R = PKT$

D. $R = KT + P$ E. $R = \frac{KT}{P}$

Translate the word problem below into an equation; then solve.

25. Pam and Sue left their house at the same time and headed in opposite directions. After 4 hours, they were 440 miles apart. If Pam drove 10 mph faster than Sue, how fast did Sue drive?
(21)

Chapter 14 Test

1. **(105)** A relationship between variables can be shown with a table, an equation, or a picture, which is called a graph.

2. **(106)** The graph of every first-degree equation with two variables is a straight line.

3. **(106)** A line with a positive slope slants upward (from left to right) and a line with a negative slope slants downward (from left to right).

Turn each ordered pair below into a point on a coordinate plane. (Remember, the *x*-value is always listed first.)

4. **(106)** $(2, -3)$

5. **(106)** $(-1, 4)$

Select the fully simplified form of each expression below.

6. **(101)** $(-2x^3y^4)(-7x^2y^5)$

A. $-5xy$
B. $-14x^5y^9$
C. $-9x^5y^9$
D. $14x^5y^9$
E. $14x^6y^{20}$

7. **(94)** $3x^2y^3 + 4xy - 6x^2y^3 - 8xy$

A. $-3x^2y^3 + (-4xy)$
B. $-18x^4y^9 - 32x^2y^2$
C. $12x^3y^4 - 48x^3y^4$
D. $7x^3y^4 - 14x^3y^4$
E. $3x^2y^3 + 4xy$

Multiply or divide (as indicated) the fractions and select the simplified answer below.

8. **(97)** $\frac{12x^2y^2}{z^2} \cdot \frac{xz}{4x^3y}$

A. $\frac{12x^2y^2 + xz}{z^2 + 4x^3y}$
B. $\frac{3y}{xz}$
C. $\frac{8x^3y}{z}$
D. $\frac{3y}{z}$
E. $\frac{x^3}{3z^3}$

9. **(100)** $\dfrac{x^2y^2}{x^2+2xy+y^2}\cdot\dfrac{x^2-y^2}{x^3y^3}$

A. $\dfrac{x-y}{xy}$
B. $\dfrac{x-y}{x^2y+xy^2}$
C. $\dfrac{x^2y^2+x^2-y^2}{x^2+2xy+y^2+x^3y^3}$
D. $\dfrac{x-y}{x^2+y^2}$
E. $\dfrac{1}{x^2+y^2}$

Solve each equation below. (Estimate any irrational answers to two decimal places.)

10. **(33)** $2(x-7)+3x=6$

11. **(58)** $\dfrac{x+4}{x+5}=\dfrac{2}{3}$

12. **(76)** $x^2=21$

For the two-variable equation $y=5x-3$, find the matching y value for each x value below.

13. **(87)** $x=1 \quad y=?$

14. **(87)** $x=-\dfrac{1}{5} \quad y=?$

Answer each question below.

15. **(92)** In the equation $z=\dfrac{x^2}{3y}$, find the value of z when $x=9$ and $y=-3$.

16. **(103)** Which choice below represents the equation $\dfrac{J}{H}=G+\dfrac{I}{H}$ after it has been solved for H?

A. $H=\dfrac{J-I}{G}$
B. $H=\dfrac{I}{J+G}$
C. $H=\dfrac{G}{IJ}$
D. $H=\dfrac{J}{G+I}$
E. $H=\dfrac{G}{J-I}$

Select the shape of the graph of each two-variable equation below.

17. **(107)** $y=3x^2$

A Two-humped curve
B. Line
C. Parabola
D. Circle
E. Square

18. $y = \frac{1}{2}x + 4$
(107)

A. Parabola　　B. Two-humped curve　　C. Circle
D. Square　　E. Line

19. $y + 2x = 1$
(107)

A. Line　　B. Two-humped curve　　C. Parabola
D. Circle　　E. Square

Find the x and y-intercepts of each two-variable equation below.

20. $y = 5 + x$
(108)

21. $y - 2x = 6$
(108)

Select the graph of each two-variable equation below.

22. $y = \frac{1}{3}x + 2$
(108)

A.

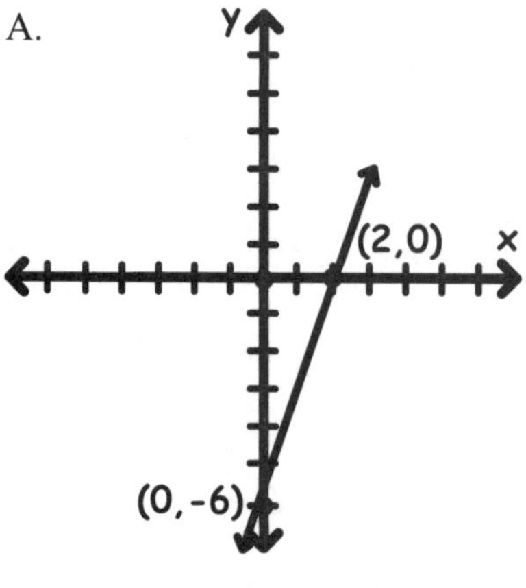

B.

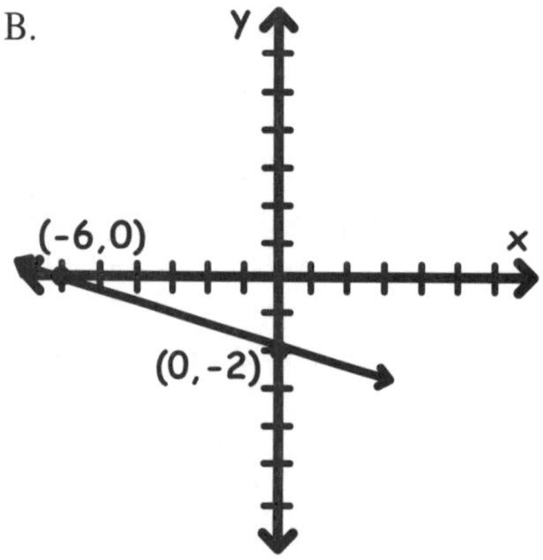

C.

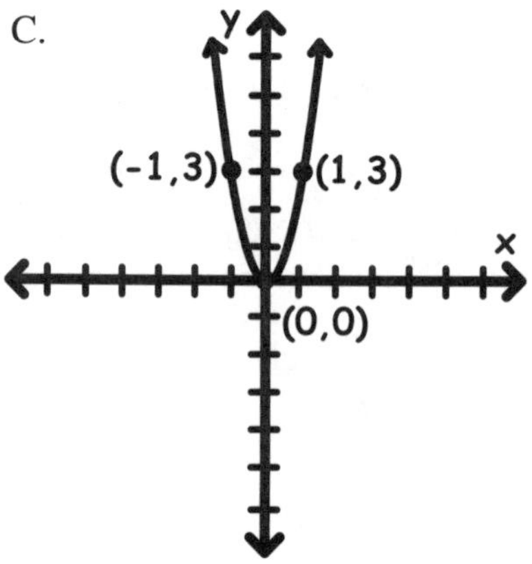

D.

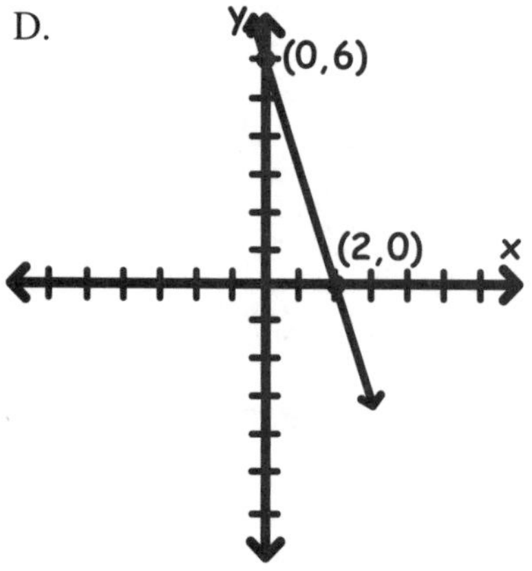

E.

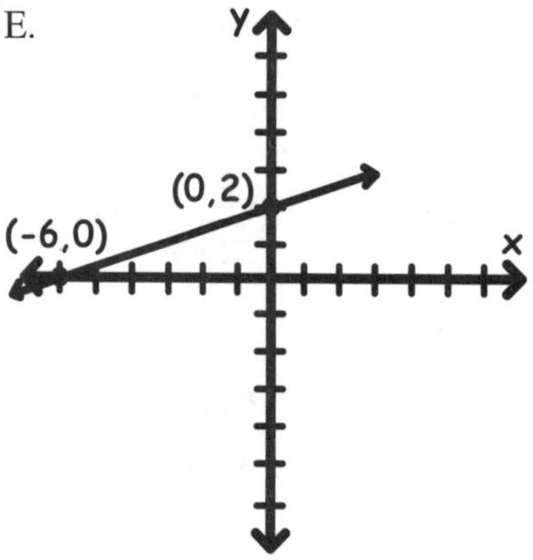

23. $y - 4x = 4$
(108)

A.

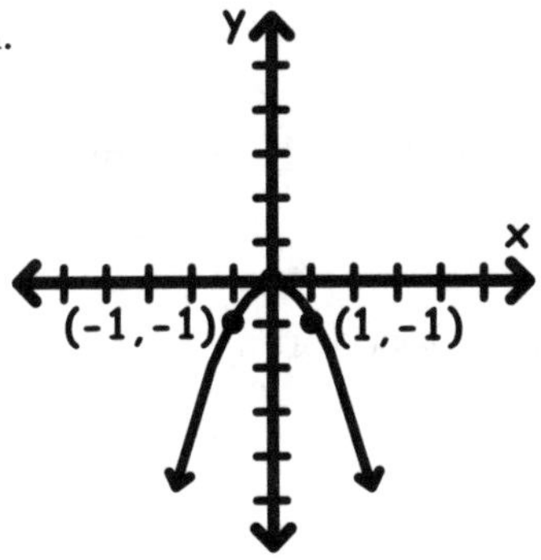

B.

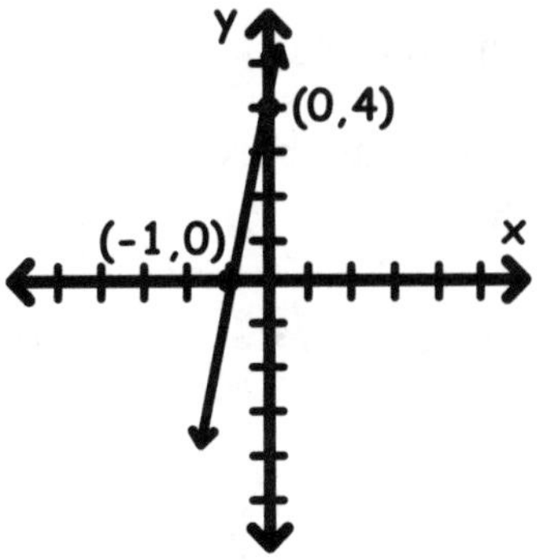

C.

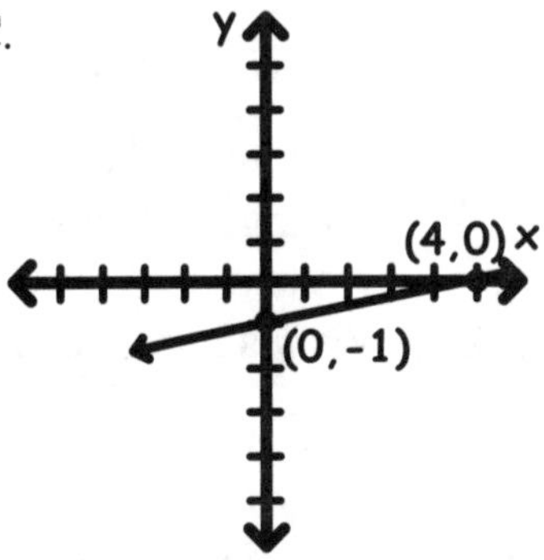

D.

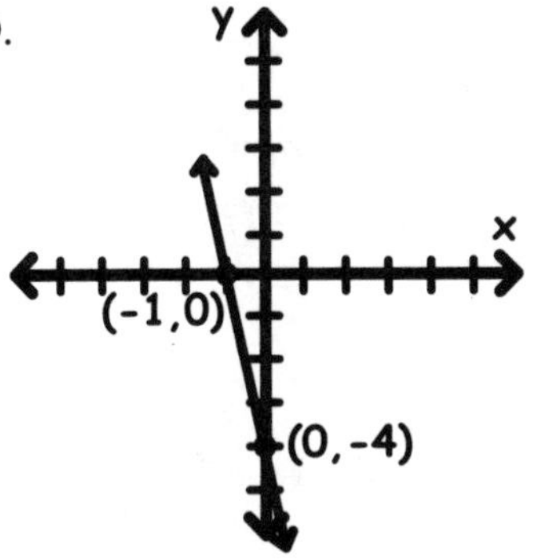

E.

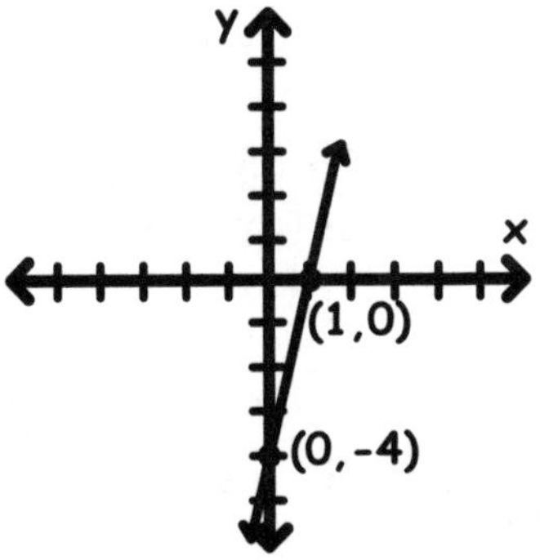

Translate the word problem below into an equation; then solve.

24. Mrs. Henson's rectangular afghan is 2 feet longer than it is wide. If the afghan has an area of 24 square feet, what is its width? (Remember, the area of a rectangle is its length *times* its width.)
(23)

Chapter 15 Test

Tell whether each sentence below is True or False.

1. (110) The rate of change between the variables of a two-variable equation is the amount that y changes when x goes up by 1.

2. (112) When a linear equation is in the form $y = mx + b$, it is in point-slope form.

Select the factored form of each expression below.

3. (99) $ay^3 + by^2$

A. $y^2(a+by)$ B. $y^2(a+b)$ C. $aby^2(by+a)$
D. $y^2(ay+b)$ E. $y^3(a+by)$

4. (83) $x^2 - 3x - 28$

A. $(x+28)(x-1)$ B. $(x-7)(x+4)$ C. $(x+7)(x-4)$
D. $(x-14)(x+2)$ E. $(x-28)(x+1)$

Distribute in the expressions and select the simplified answer below.

5. (96) $2xy(4x^2 + 5y)$

A. $8x^2y+10xy$ B. $8x^3y+10x^2y^3$ C. $8x^3y+10xy^2$
D. $6x^3y+7xy^2$ E. $40x^3y^2$

6. (96) $(x+2b)(x-4b)$

A. $x^2-2bx-8b^2$ B. $2x-2b$ C. $x^2+2bx-8b^2$
D. x^2-8b^2 E. $x^2-8bx-8b^2$

Tell whether each pair of expressions below is equivalent.

7. (96) $x^2 + 2ax + a^2$ and $(x+a)(x+a)$

8. (96) $9p^2 - 25q^2$ and $(3p+5q)(3p-5q)$

Solve each equation below. (Estimate any irrational answers to two decimal places.)

9. (28) $\frac{3}{5}x - \frac{1}{5}x = -20$

10. (33) $7(x+3) - 5x = 7$

11. (80) $2x^2 + 4 = 34$

Answer each question below.

12. (92) In the equation $z = \frac{8x}{y^2}$, find the value of z when $x = 64$ and $y = -4$.

13. (103) Which choice below represents the equation $q = ap + bp$ after it has been solved for p?

A. $p = qa + qb$

B. $p = \frac{q}{a+b}$

C. $p = \frac{a+b}{q}$

D. $p = \frac{q+ap}{b}$

E. $p = \frac{q-ap}{b}$

Find the rate of change (slope) for each two-variable equation below.

14. (110) $2y = -3x$

15. (111) $y = 0x - 9$

Find the slope (rate of change) of each line below.

16. (112) Slope of A

17. (112) Slope of B

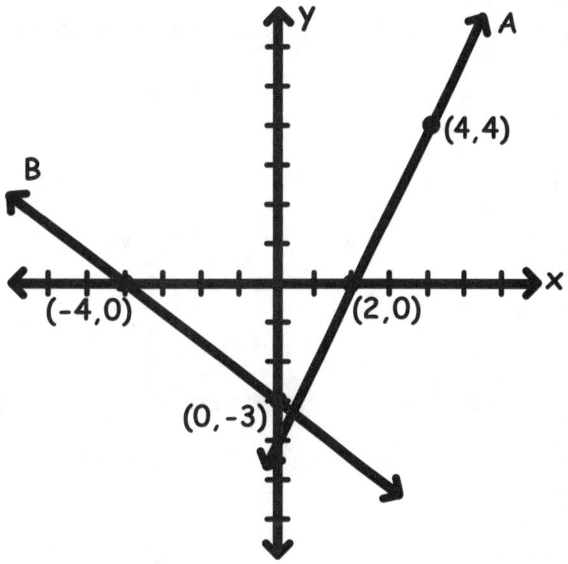

Tell the slope and y-intercept of the graph of each linear equation below.

18. (112) $y-3x=-1$

19. (112) $y+\frac{1}{4}x=5$

20. (112) $-3x+2y=8$

Select the equation for each line described below.

21. (113) The line crossing the point $(3,1)$ and with slope = 4.

A. $y-4=3(x-1)$
B. $y-3=2(x-1)$
C. $y-1=4(x-3)$
D. $y-3=4(x-1)$
E. $y-1=-4(x-3)$

22. (113) The line crossing the point $(2,7)$ and with slope = -2.

A. $y+7=-2(x+2)$
B. $y-7=1(x-2)$
C. $y-2=-2(x-7)$
D. $y+2=2(x-7)$
E. $y-7=-2(x-2)$

Select the graph of each equation below (on a coordinate plane).

23. (112) $y=-\frac{1}{2}x+4$

A.

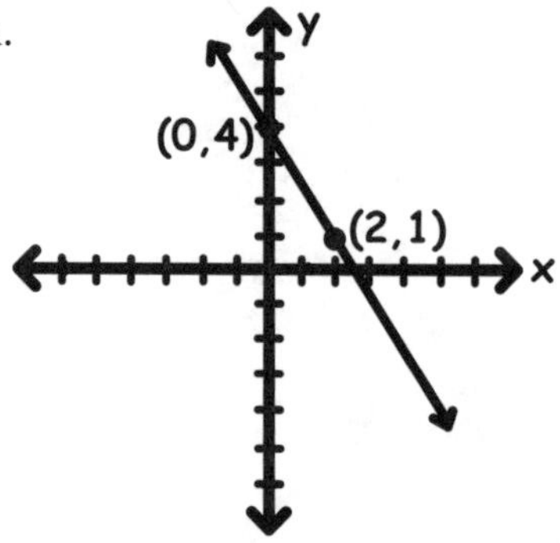

B.

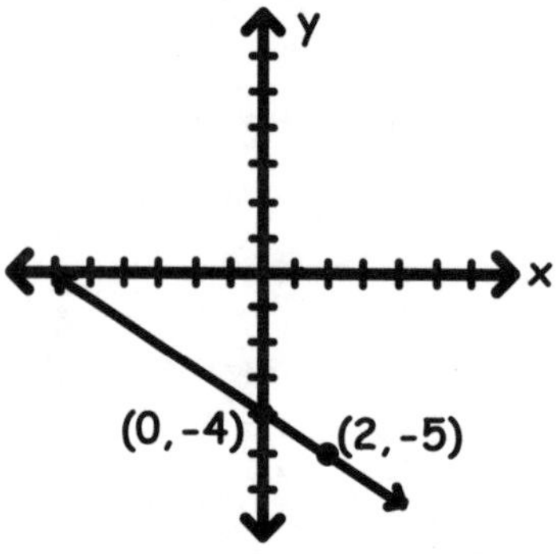

C.

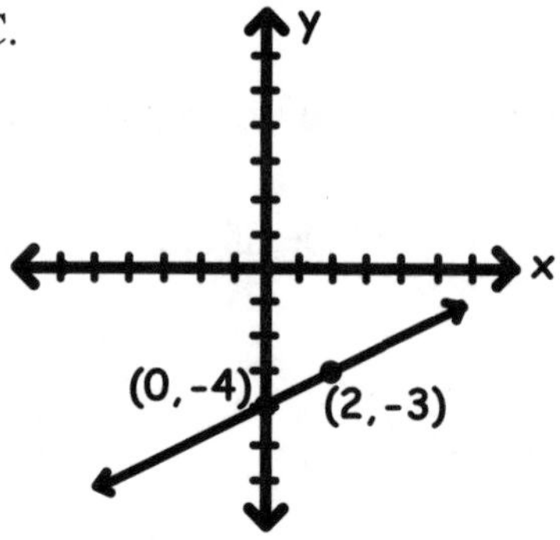

D.

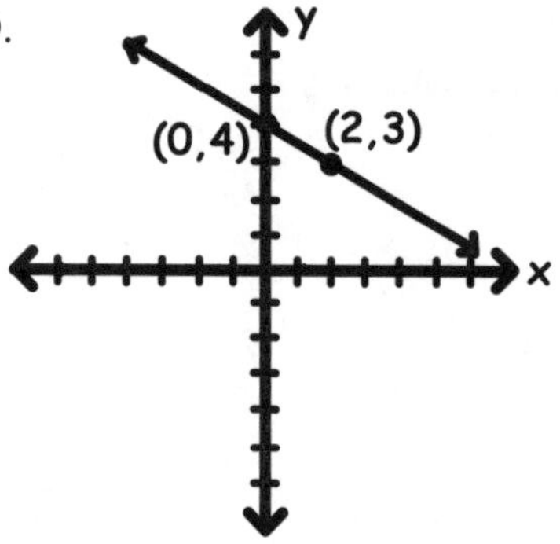

E.

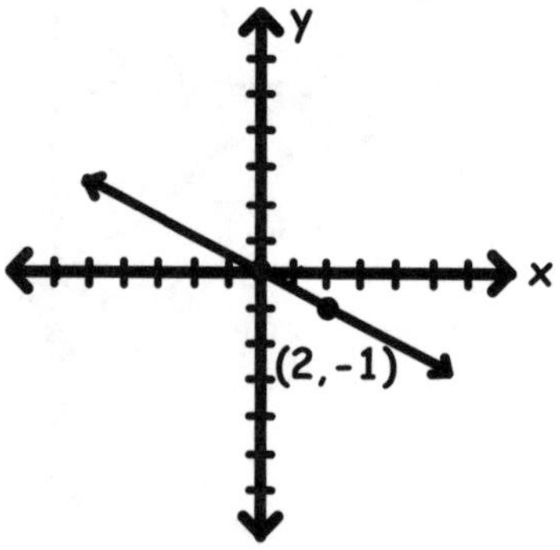

24. $y = 3$
(111)

A.

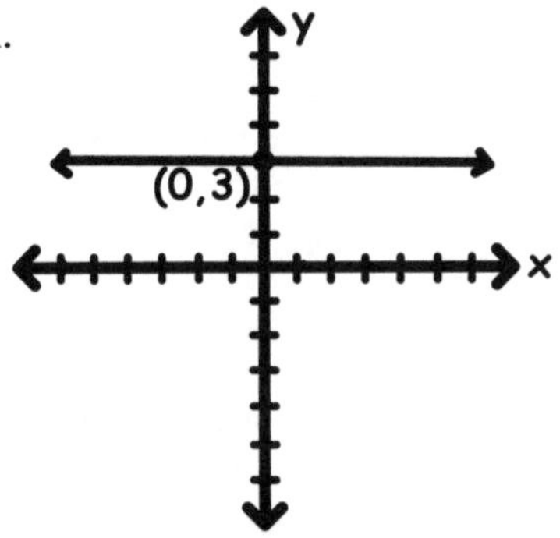

B.

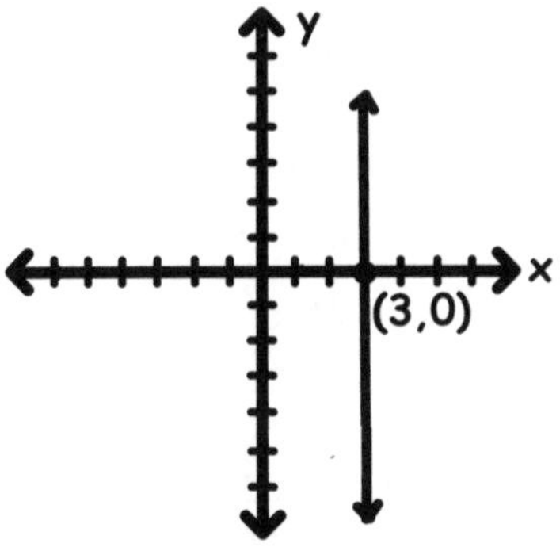

C.

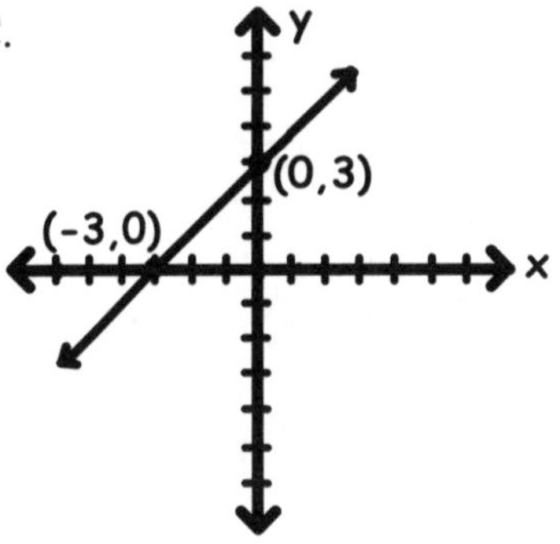

D.

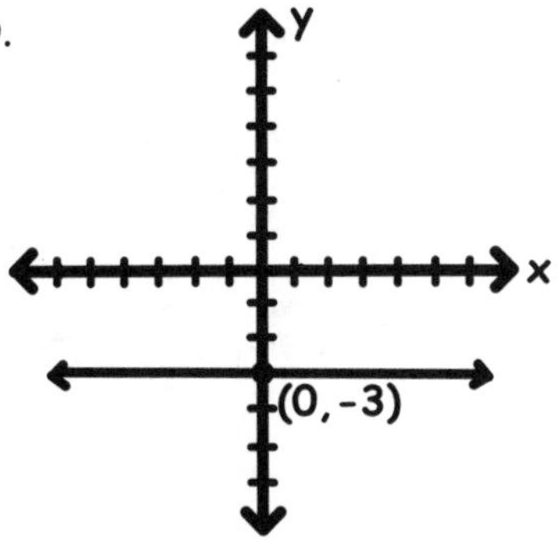

E.

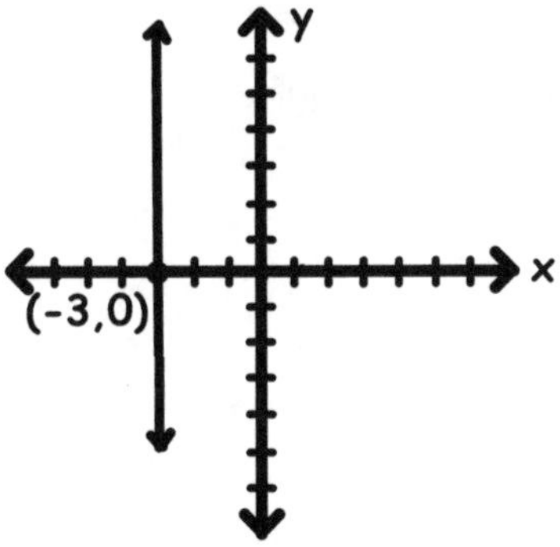

Translate the word problem below into an equation; then solve.

25. Ralph can lay down a floor tile in 5 seconds. Bob can lay down a floor tile in 4 seconds. If both boys work together, how many seconds would it take them to install 450 floor tiles?
(29)

Chapter 16 Test

Tell whether each sentence below is True or False.

1. (110) Two equations that represent a single problem are together called a "system" of equations.

2. (112) There is no way to graph a system of equations.

3. (112) If you get a false equation when trying to solve a system of two linear equations, the system's graph must be two parallel lines.

Select the factored form of each expression below.

4. (98) $8x^4y^5 - 32x^3y^2$

A. $8xy^2(x^3y^3 - 4x^2)$ B. $4x^4y^5(2 - 8xy^3)$ C. $8x^3y^2(xy^3 - 4)$

D. $32x^3y^2(4xy^3 - 1)$ E. $8x^4y^2(y^3 - 4x)$

5. (100) $y^2 - 81$

A. $(y-9)(y-9)$ B. $(y+9)(y-9)$ C. $(y+81)(y-81)$

D. $(y+40.5)(y-40.5)$ E. $(y+9)(y+9)$

Select the fully reduced form of each fraction below

6. (83) $\dfrac{p^2 - 4p - 21}{p^2 - 2p - 35}$

A. $\dfrac{p+5}{p+3}$ B. $\dfrac{p+3}{p-7}$ C. $\dfrac{p+3}{p+5}$

D. $\dfrac{p+7}{p+5}$ E. $\dfrac{p-7}{p+5}$

7. (100) $\dfrac{x^2 - y^2}{x^2 + 2xy + y^2}$

A. $\dfrac{x+y}{x-y}$ B. $\dfrac{1}{x+y}$ C. $x-y$

D. 1 E. $\dfrac{x-y}{x+y}$

Add or subtract (as indicated) the fractions and select the simplified answer below.

8. (102) $\dfrac{s+t}{12st}+\dfrac{s-t}{4st}$

A. $\dfrac{2s-t}{6st}$ B. $\dfrac{s^2-t^2}{48s^2t^2}$ C. $\dfrac{s-2t}{6st}$

D. $\dfrac{s+t}{16st}$ E. $\dfrac{1}{8t}$

9. (102) $\dfrac{y}{bx}+\dfrac{b}{xy}-\dfrac{x}{by}$

A. $\dfrac{y^2+bx-x^2}{xy}$ B. $\dfrac{bx+xy-by}{xy}$ C. $\dfrac{y^2+b^2-x^2}{bxy}$

D. $\dfrac{y+b-x}{bxy}$ E. $\dfrac{bx+xy-by}{bxy}$

Tell whether each pair of expressions below is equivalent.

10. (101) $(-ab^2)(a^2b)(ab)$ and $-3ab^2$

11. (100) $4m^2-9n^2$ and $(2m+3n)(2m-3n)$

Solve each quadratic (second-degree) equation below by factoring.

12. (81) $2x^2+6x=0$

13. (82) $x^2+9x+14=0$

Answer each question below.

14. (92) In the equation $p=\dfrac{4q^2}{s-2}$, find the value of p when $q=-2$ and $s=4$.

15. (103) Which choice below represents the equation $H=\dfrac{G}{f+e}$ after it has been solved for e?

A. $e=Hf-G$ B. $e=\dfrac{G-Hf}{H}$ C. $e=\dfrac{G}{H-f}$

D. $e=\dfrac{G+Hf}{H}$ E. $e=\dfrac{Gf}{H}$

Tell the slope and y-intercept of the graph of each linear equation below.

16. (112) $3y-6x-9=0$

17. (112) $-\frac{1}{2}y=5x$

Select the equation for each line below.

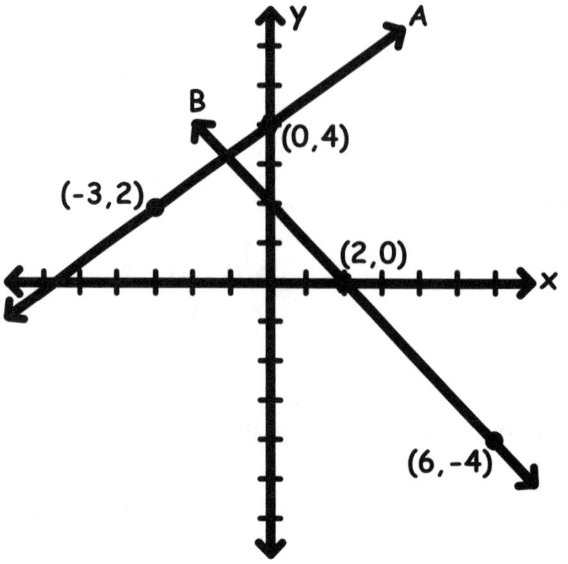

18. (113) line A

A. $y=\frac{2}{3}x+2$

B. $y=-\frac{1}{3}x+2$

C. $y=\frac{1}{3}x+4$

D. $y=\frac{2}{3}x+4$

E. $y=\frac{2}{3}x+(-3)$

19. (113) line B

A. $y-0=-1(x-2)$

B. $y-0=-2(x-2)$

C. $y-2=-1(x-0)$

D. $y-6=-3(x+4)$

E. $y-4=-1(x+6)$

Solve each system of equations below.

20. (114) $\begin{cases} 2x-5y=-2 \\ 2x+3y=14 \end{cases}$

21. (114) $\begin{cases} 3x+y=-21 \\ y=4x \end{cases}$

Select the graph of each system of equations below.

22. **(118)** $\begin{cases} y = -3x + 6 \\ y - 2x = 1 \end{cases}$

A.

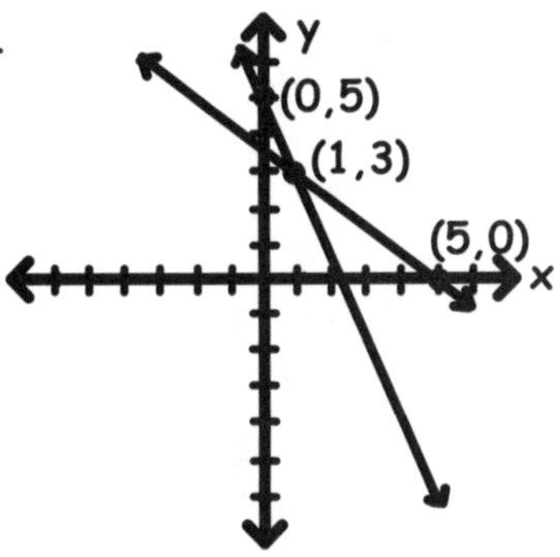

B.

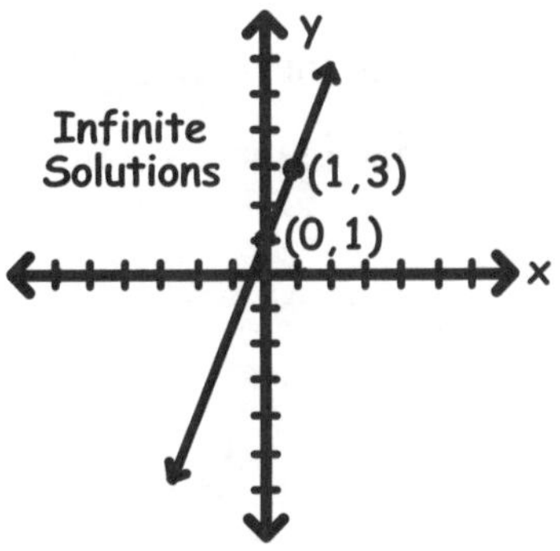

C.

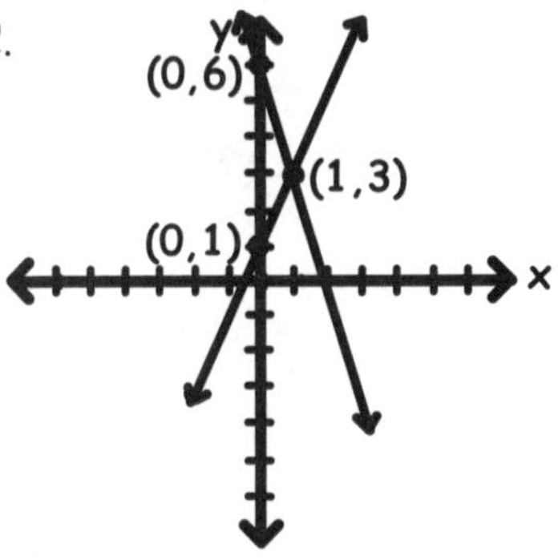

D.

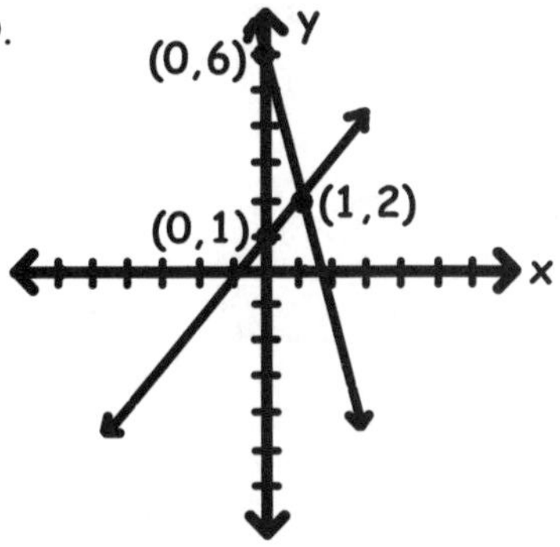

E.

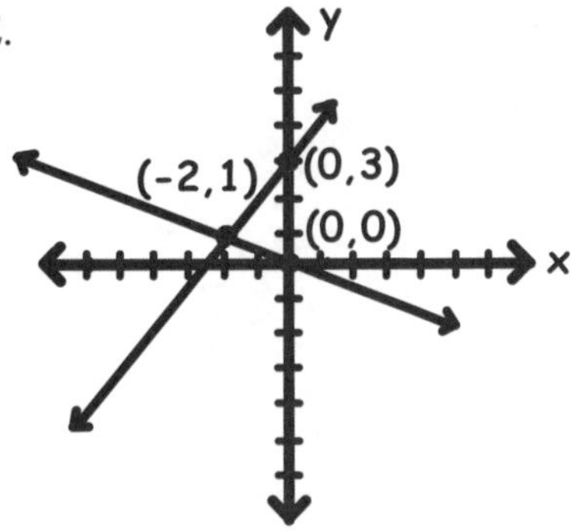

23. **(118)** $\begin{cases} y = -x - 3 \\ y + x = 5 \end{cases}$

A.

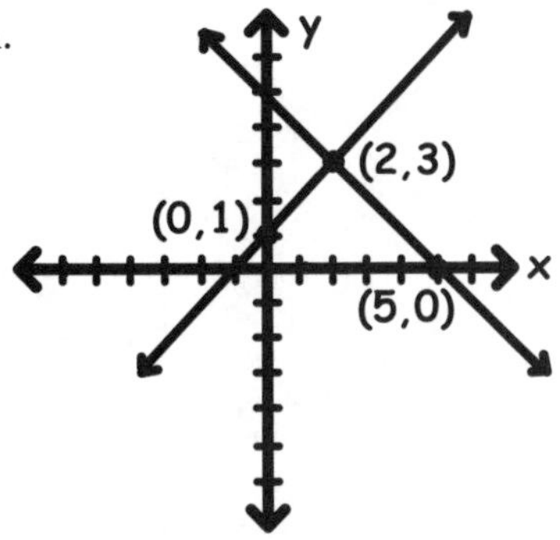

B.

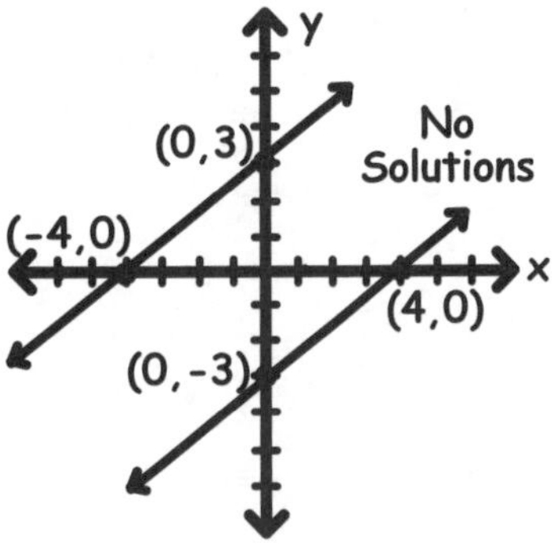

C.

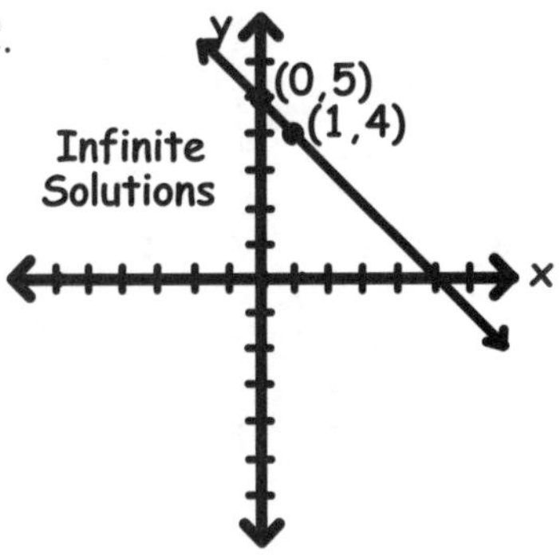

D.

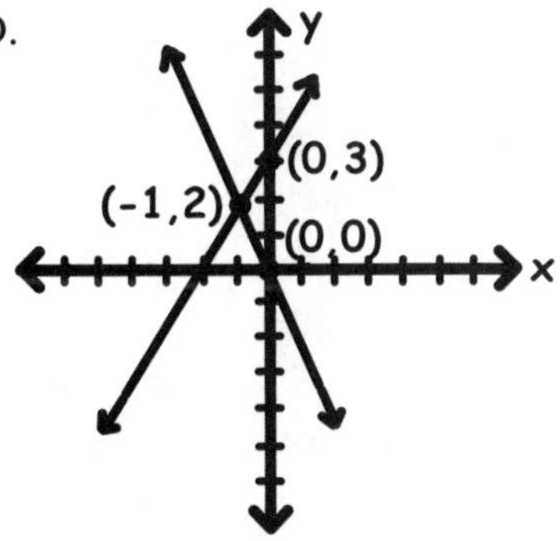

E.

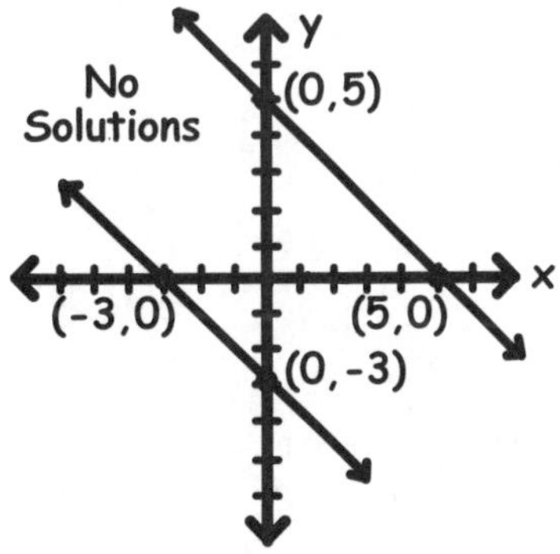

Translate the word problem below into a system of equations; then solve.

24. (116) Tickets to *Gone With the Wind*, at the Classic Movie House, cost $4.50 for adults and $2 for children. If 45 people attended the Saturday matinee showing and the Classic Movie House sold $162.50 worth of tickets

a.) How many adults attended the showing?

b.) How many children attended the showing?

Chapter 17 Test

Tell whether each sentence below is True or False.

1. (121) Inequalities can never be solved by undoing.

2. (121) When multiplying or dividing both sides of an inequality by a negative number, the direction of the inequality symbol must be flipped.

Simplify each irrational expression below. Select the best possible choice.

3. (126) $\sqrt{20}$

A. $4\sqrt{5}$ B. $2\sqrt{10}$ C. $2\sqrt{5}$
D. $5\sqrt{2}$ E. $\sqrt{10}$

4. (123) $\sqrt[3]{3}\cdot\sqrt[3]{6}$

A. $2\sqrt[3]{3}$ B. $3\sqrt[3]{6}$ C. $\sqrt[3]{9}$
D. $\sqrt[3]{18}$ E. $3\sqrt[3]{3}$

5. (126) $7\sqrt{2}+\sqrt{50}$

A. $12\sqrt{2}$ B. 70 C. 24
D. $35\sqrt{2}$ E. $7\sqrt{52}$

Simplify the irrational expression below.

6. (124) $\dfrac{\sqrt{35}}{\sqrt{7}}$

Select the correct word description and graph of the solutions to each inequality below.

7. $x > -5$
(120)

A. All of the numbers greater than –5

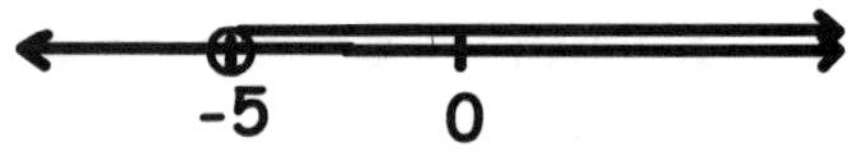

B. All of the numbers less than or equal to 5

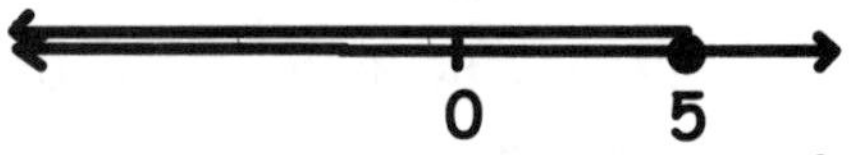

C. All of the numbers greater than or equal to –5

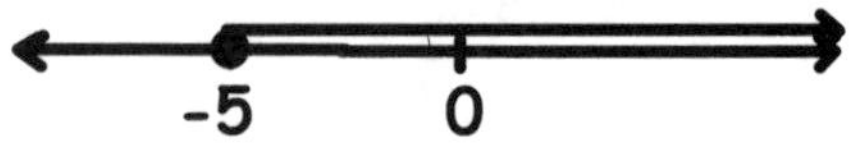

D. All of the numbers less than –5

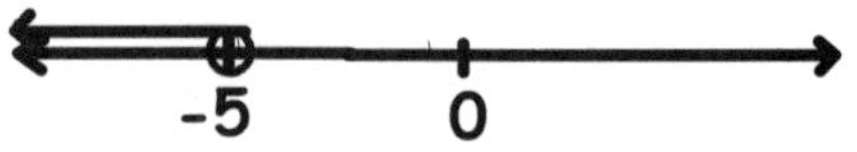

E. All of the numbers greater than 5

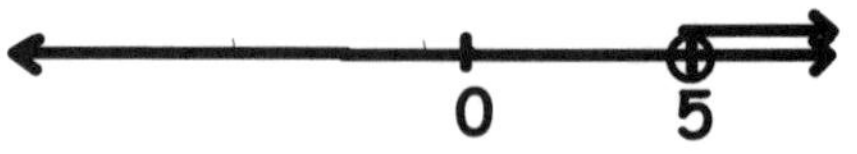

8. $x \leq 7$
(120)

A. All of the numbers less than 7

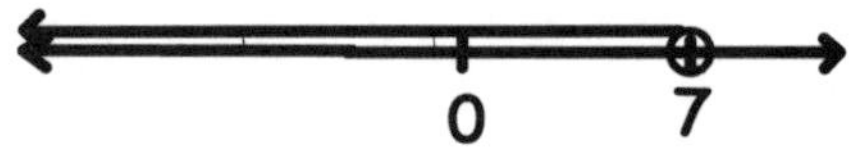

B. All of the numbers greater than or equal to 7

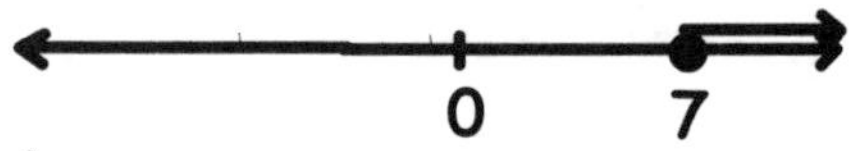

C. All of the numbers less than or equal to –7

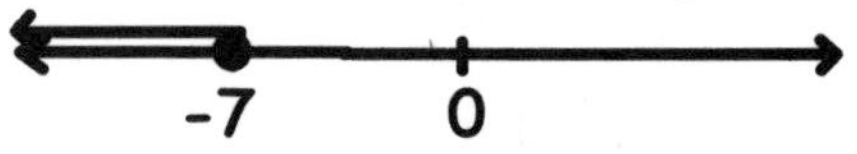

D. All of the numbers less than or equal to 7

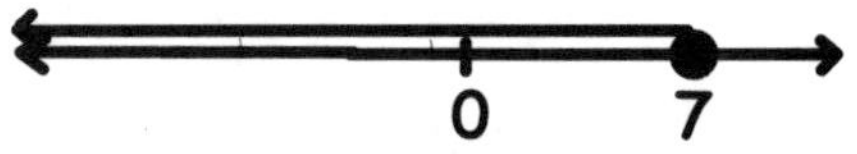

E. All of the numbers greater than –7

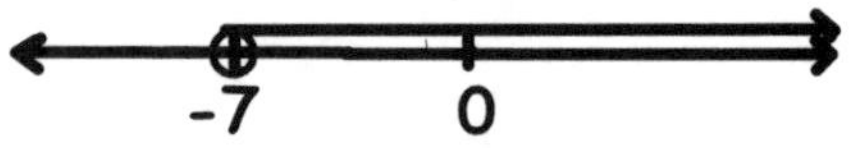

Select an inequality for each statement below.

9. A quantity x that can equal any number above -17.
(120)

A. $x > 17$ B. $x \geq -17$ C. $x = -17$
D. $x < -17$ E. $x > -17$

10. A quantity y that can equal 3.5 or any number below 3.5.
(120)

A. $y \leq 3.5$ B. $y < 3.5$ C. $y \geq 3.5$
D. $y \leq -3.5$ E. $y > 3.5$

Find the slope and y-intercept of each equation below.

11. $y - 15x = 2$
(110)

12. $y + \frac{1}{6}x = 0$
(110)

Solve each system of equations below.

13. (114) $\begin{cases} 3x-8y=-39 \\ x+2y=15 \end{cases}$

14. (114) $\begin{cases} y=-2x \\ y=-5x-21 \end{cases}$

Solve each inequality below and select your answer from the choices given.

15. (121) $2x+9<3$

A. $x<-12$ B. $x<-3$ C. $x>-3$
D. $x<6$ E. $x<-6$

16. (122) $4y-1>\frac{y+7}{2}$

A. $y>\frac{8}{9}$ B. $y>\frac{6}{7}$ C. $y>\frac{8}{7}$
D. $y<\frac{4}{7}$ E. $y>\frac{9}{7}$

17. (122) $-4(x+2)\leq 3(x-5)$

A. $x\geq\frac{23}{7}$ B. $x\geq 1$ C. $x\geq -1$
D. $x\leq -1$ E. $x\leq 1$

For each two-variable inequality below, put the number 4 in for *x* and select the set of matching numbers for *y*.

18. (128) $y>x-2$

A. $y>4$ B. $y<2$ C. $y>2$
D. $y<6$ E. $y>-2$

19. (128) $y\leq -3x-6$

A. $y\geq -18$ B. $y\leq -\frac{10}{3}$ C. $y\leq -6$
D. $y\geq -6$ E. $y\leq -18$

For each problem below, select the choice that represents the two-variable inequality after it has been solved for y in terms of x.

20. $x > \dfrac{y-4}{3}$
(128)

A. $y < 3x+4$ B. $y > 3x+4$ C. $y > 3x-4$

D. $y < 3x-4$ E. $y < -3x-4$

21. $-6y \le -4(y-3x)$
(128)

A. $y \le 6x$ B. $y \ge 6x$ C. $y \le 12x+2$

D. $y \le -6x$ E. $y \ge -6x$

Select the graph of each system of inequalities below.

22. $\begin{cases} y \ge -x \\ y \le -x-3 \end{cases}$
(130)

A.
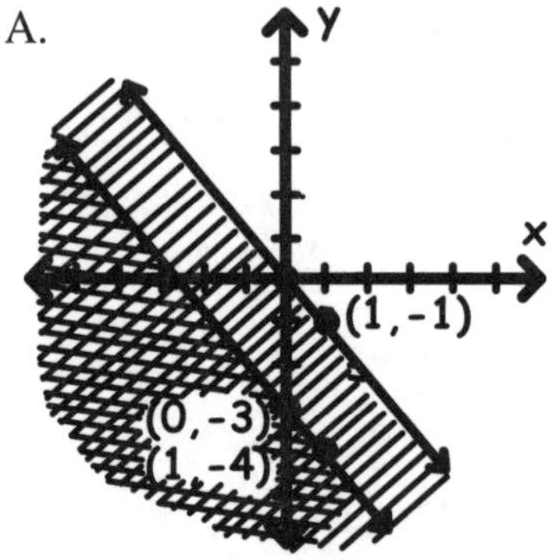

B.
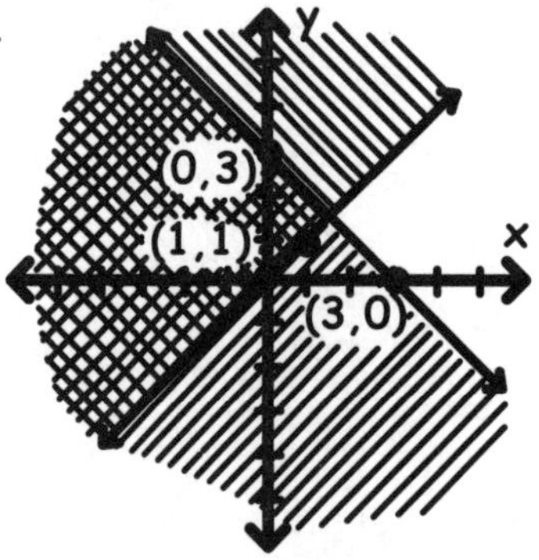

C.
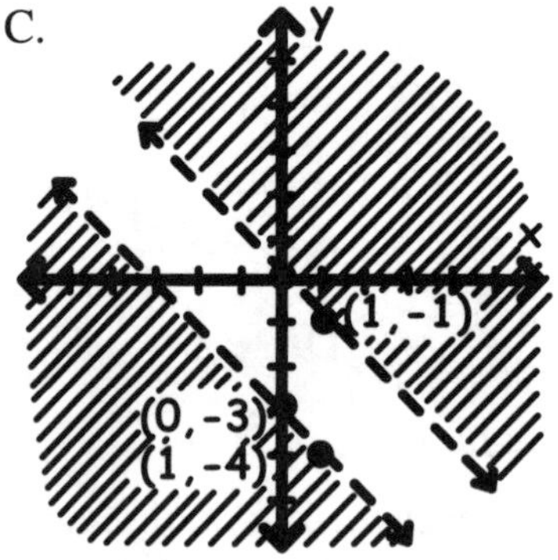

D.
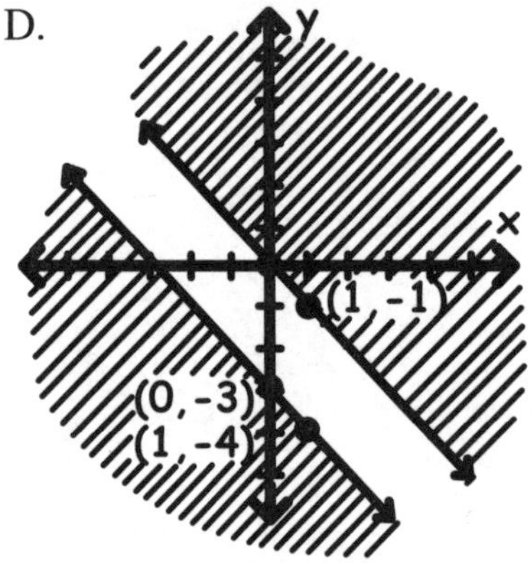

E.
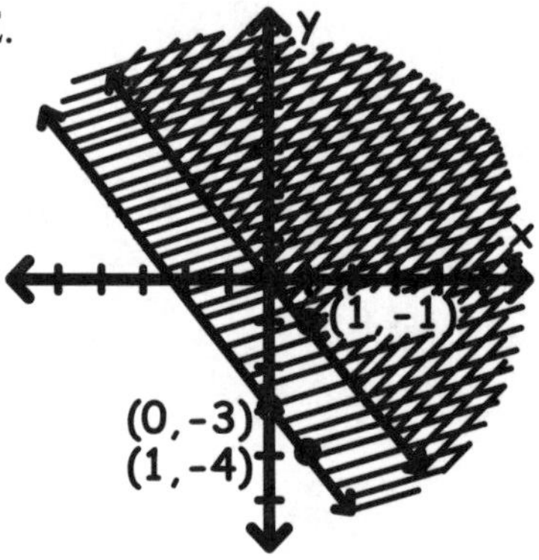

23. (130) $\begin{cases} y > \frac{1}{3}x \\ y < -2x + 4 \end{cases}$

A.

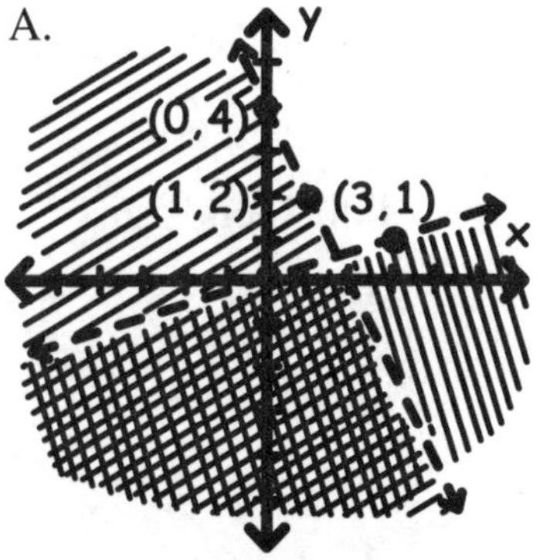

B.

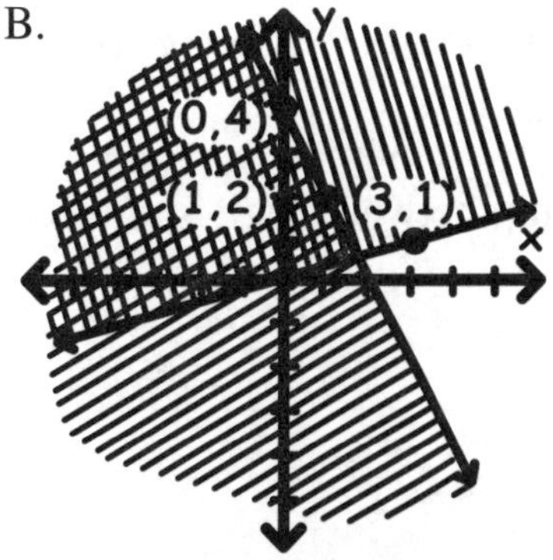

C.

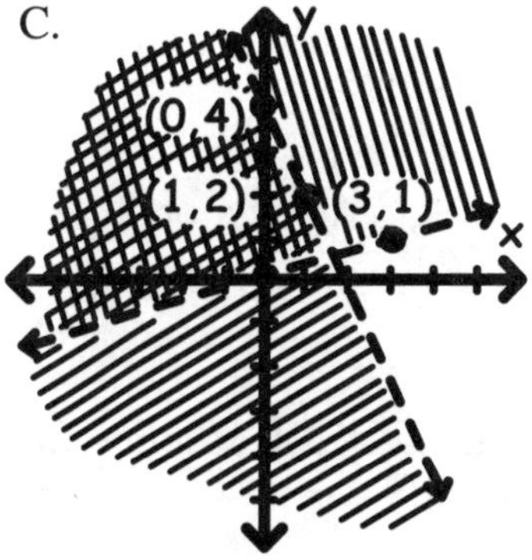

D.

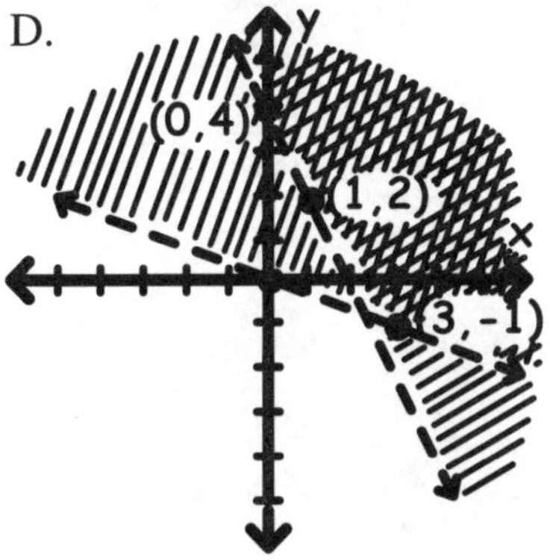

E.

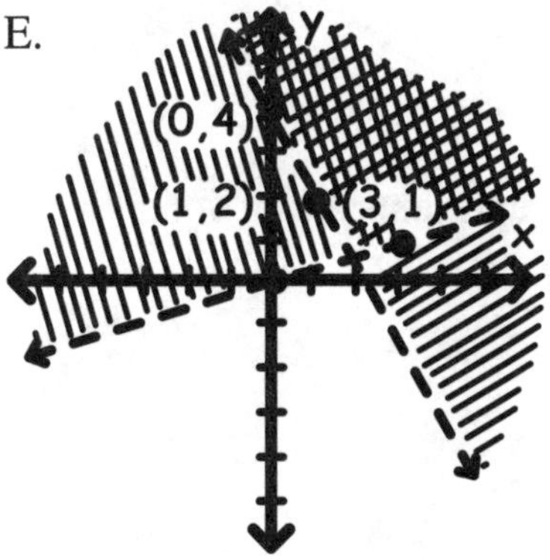

Translate the word problem below into an equation; then solve.

24. (41) Mr. Max and Mr. Min start off in the same place and head in opposite directions. Mr. Max is traveling at 60 mph and Mr. Min at 55 mph. How long will it be before the two are 345 miles apart?

Chapter 18 Test

Tell whether each sentence below is True or False.

1. (131) The measure of the magnitude of a quantity (ignoring its sign) is called its absolute value.

2. (134) A function is a relationship between variables where for each x value, there's just one matching y value.

Calculate each absolute value below.

3. (131) $|4-12|$

4. (131) $\left|\frac{1}{6}-2\right|$

Tell whether each graph below represents a function.

5. (134)

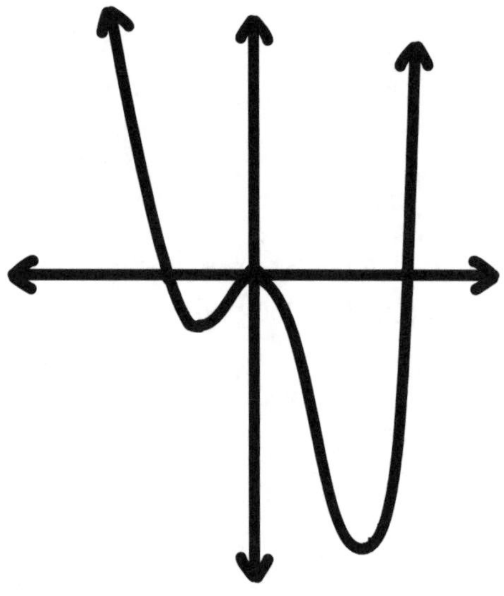

6. (134)

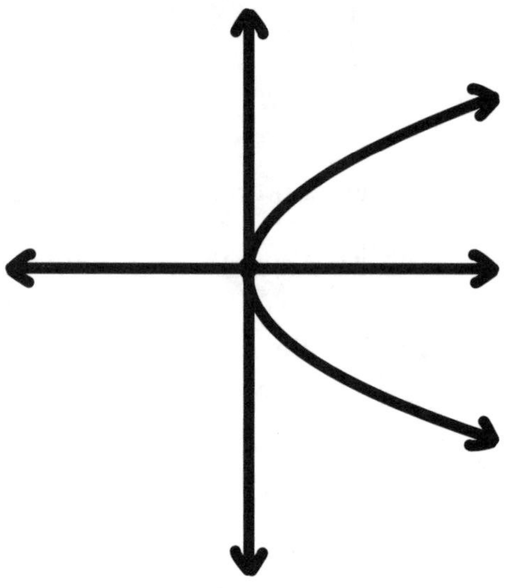

Tell whether the relationship in each table below represents a function.

7. (134)

x	y
-5	-2
-4	1
0	4
3	-7
4	1
5	3

8. (134)

x	y
3	8
-1	6
0	-3
1	-4
2	0
3	1

Select the domain or range of each function below.

9. (134) $y = \dfrac{1}{x+6}$

A. Domain: All real numbers except 0
B. Domain: All real numbers except 6
C. Domain: All real numbers except 1
D. Domain: All real numbers except −6
E. Domain: All real numbers

10. (134) $y = 9x^2$

A. Domain: All real numbers greater or equal to 9; Range: All real numbers
B. Domain: All real numbers; Range: All positive real numbers and 0
C. Domain: All real numbers; Range: All real numbers greater or equal to 9
D. Domain: All real numbers greater or equal to 9; Range: All positive real numbers
E. Domain: All positive real numbers and 0; Range: All real numbers

Find the indicated value of the dependent variable for the function $f(x) = x^2 + 4x - 3$.

11. (135) $f(3)$

12. (135) $f(-2)$

Solve each system of equations below.

13. (116) $\begin{cases} x - y = 3 \\ 4x + y = 7 \end{cases}$

14. (116) $\begin{cases} 2x - 3y = -13 \\ 4x + 5y = 7 \end{cases}$

For each two-variable inequality below, put the number -3 in for x and select the set of matching numbers for y.

15. $y > \frac{1}{6}x + \frac{5}{2}$
(128)

A. $y < -2$ B. $y > 3$ C. $y > \frac{9}{2}$

D. $y > \frac{13}{6}$ E. $y > 2$

16. $4x - 5y \leq -3$
(128)

A. $y \leq -\frac{9}{2}$ B. $y \geq -3$ C. $y \geq -\frac{9}{5}$

D. $y \leq -\frac{5}{9}$ E. $y \leq -3$

Solve each inequality below and select your answer from the choices given.

17. $7y + 2 \leq -3y - 8$
(122)

A. $y \leq -\frac{5}{2}$ B. $y \leq -1$ C. $y \leq -\frac{3}{5}$

D. $y \geq -\frac{5}{2}$ E. $y \geq -1$

18. $-2(x-5) > -6(x+4)$
(122)

A. $x > \frac{17}{2}$ B. $x > \frac{9}{4}$ C. $x > -\frac{17}{2}$

D. $x < \frac{17}{4}$ E. $x > \frac{7}{2}$

For each problem below, select the choice that represents the two-variable inequality after it has been solved for y in terms of x.

19. $5x + 3y > 4$
(128)

A. $y > \frac{4-5x}{3}$ B. $y > \frac{1}{2}$ C. $y < \frac{4-5x}{3}$

D. $y < \frac{4+5x}{3}$ E. $y > \frac{4+5x}{3}$

20. $x - \frac{y}{3} \le -4x + 2$
(128)

A. $y \ge 15x - 6$ B. $y \ge \frac{5}{3}x - \frac{2}{3}$ C. $y \le -15x + 6$

D. $y \le -\frac{5}{3}x + \frac{2}{3}$ E. $y \le 15x - 6$

Solve each absolute value equation below.

21. $|4x| = 20$
(133)

22. $|x - 5| = 8$
(133)

23. $|6x + 42| = 0$
(133)

Translate the word problem below into an inequality; then solve. Select your answer from the choices.

24. Two publishers have offered Melanie Thompson a deal on her new book *Sugar-Free Culinary Classics*. The first has offered to pay her \$82,000 up front and a \$5.50 royalty for every book it sells. The second has offered to pay \$68,000 up front and a \$6.75 royalty for every book it sells. Over what range of book sales will Melanie make more from the second publisher than she will from the first?
(122)

A. Less than 11,200 books B. More than 13,400 books
C. More than 11,200 books D. Less than 13,400 books
E. More than 11,200 but less than 13,400 books

Chapter 19 Test

Tell whether each sentence below is True or False.

1. (136) The study of large groups of numbers is called statistics.

2. (139) Probability is a measure of how certain something is to happen.

Answer each question below.

3. (135) For the function $f(x) = x + 5$, find the matching value for x when $f(x) = 8$.

4. (135) For the function $f(x) = -12x + 7$, find the matching value for x when $f(x) = 17$. Write your answer as a fraction.

Solve each equation below.

5. (41) $7(x-2) = 4x + 8$

6. (58) $\dfrac{x+3}{x-6} = 4$

Solve each absolute value equation below.

7. (133) $|-3x| = 12$

8. (133) $\left|2x + \dfrac{1}{4}\right| = 1$

For each problem below, select the choice that represents the two-variable inequality after it has been solved for y in terms of x.

9. (128) $7y - 2x \geq 5$

A. $y \geq \dfrac{-2x+5}{7}$

B. $y \geq \dfrac{2x+5}{7}$

C. $y \leq \dfrac{2x+5}{7}$

D. $7y \geq 2x + 5$

E. $y \leq \dfrac{7x-5}{2}$

10. (128) $\frac{1}{3}y - \frac{1}{2}y < x + 5$

A. $y > -6x - 30$ B. $y > -6x - 1$ C. $y < 6x + 30$

D. $y < -6x + 5$ E. $y < -6x - 30$

The table below shows the number of minutes it took for each contestant to eat 50 hotdogs in an eating contest.

Number of Minutes to Eat 50 Hotdogs

20.1	19.6	18.0	17.8	25.2	18.7
21.9	16.3	25.4	20.5	17.8	19.3

11. (136) Find the median of the data.

12. (136) Find the mean and range of the data.

The table below shows the electricity usage in kilowatts of several households in a neighborhood last month. Select the best measure of central tendency of this data.

Electricity Usage Last Month

498	500	354	370	682
423	544	450	508	1,854
639	605	497	386	617

13. (136) A. Mean B. Median C. Mode

Use the box and whisker plot below to answer each of the following questions.

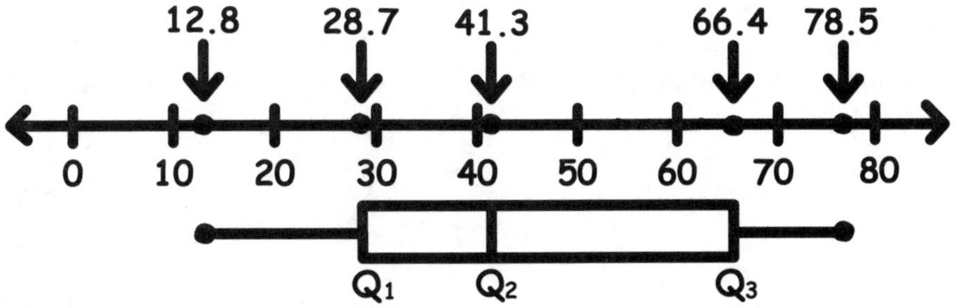

14. (137) What is the overall median of the data?

What value separates the first and the second group?

15. What is the range of the data?
(137)

Are the numbers in the two middle groups more spread out above or below the median?

The histogram below shows ranges for the number of seconds it took a group of children to solve a puzzle. Use the histogram to answer each of the following questions.

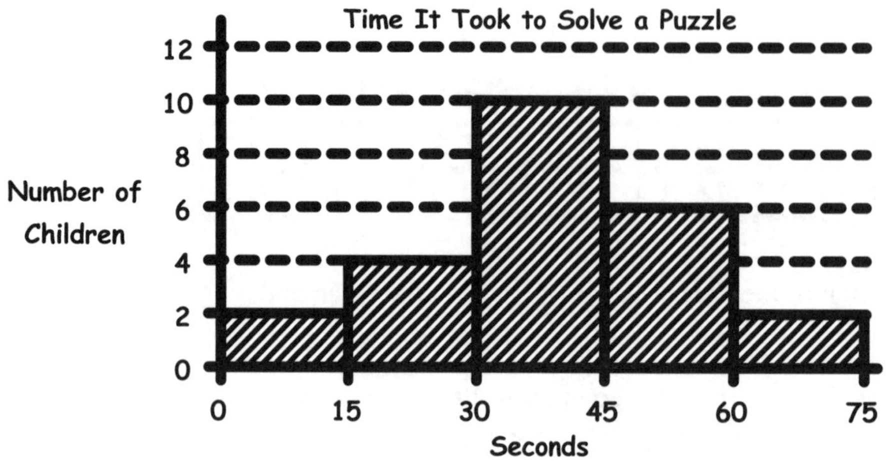

16. How many children took at least 30 seconds to solve the puzzle?
(138)

17. How many children in total are represented in this histogram?
(138)

Answer each question below using the data given in the stem-and-leaf plot. The stems represent ones and the leaves represent tenths.

18. How many numbers have a 4 for a tenths digit? Find the mode of the data.
(138)

19. Find the median and range of the data.
(138)

Stem	Leaf
0	3 4 4
2	0 1 1 3 5
3	2 2 2 6 8
4	7 9
6	6 6 7 9
7	3 4 4
9	1 2 5

1|0 = 1.0

Answer each question below.

20. (139) There are 8 tennis balls in a bag. Five of the balls are yellow and the other 3 are green What's the probability of pulling out a green ball without looking? Write your answer as a decimal.

21. (139) Find the probability of rolling a 6-sided die and getting a 3. Write your answer as a fraction.

22. (139) If three 4-sided dice were rolled, what would be the probability of getting triple 1s? Write your answer as a fraction.

23. (140) There are 4 banana smoothies, 1 strawberry smoothie and 1 watermelon smoothie in the refrigerator. Without looking, what is the probability of pulling out a banana smoothie and then another banana smoothie? (Assume that you don't put the first banana smoothie back in the refrigerator.) Write your answer as a percent.

Translate the word problem below into an equation; then solve.

24. (44) Mr. Ferrier invested \$26,000. Some was invested in bonds that made a 5% profit, and the rest was put into stocks that made an 8% profit. How much did Mr. Ferrier invest in bonds if his total profit on both types of investments was \$1,420?

CHAPTER TEST ANSWERS

Chapter 1 Test

1. True
2. True
3. True
4. D
5. C
6. Algebra
7. Arithmetic
8. D
9. C
10. 0.325
11. 19%
12. 18 feet
13. No
14. Yes
15. No
16. 19
17. $\frac{13}{8}$
18. 4.5
19. 190.4
20. 2.4
21. 287
22. $\frac{2}{3}$
23. $\frac{4}{15}$
24. $\frac{3}{14}$
25. 11.5 hours

Chapter 2 Test

1. True
2. True
3. A
4. B
5. 10
6. $-\frac{3}{4}$
7. -43
8. 1.5
9. -36
10. 0
11. 200
12. -2
13. 8
14. -4
15. 0
16. Yes
17. Yes
18. No
19. -22
20. $\frac{4}{5}$
21. 170.14
22. -93
23. -32
24. 96
25. 7.5%

Chapter 3 Test

1. False
2. True
3. E
4. E
5. B
6. 15
7. 14
8. A
9. E
10. D
11. A
12. B
13. C
14. No
15. Yes
16. D
17. D
18. B
19. 7
20. -9
21. -36
22. 6
23. 5
24. -11
25. 84 stamps

Chapter 4 Test

1. True
2. True
3. 37
4. -7
5. E
6. D
7. E
8. C
9. A
10. E
11. No
12. Yes
13. $\frac{1}{12}$ windshields per min.
14. $\frac{11}{3}$ chairs per hr.
15. 14
16. -9
17. 16
18. $\frac{1}{5}$
19. -4
20. -24
21. -6
22. 15
23. 60
24. Bill is 16; Eric is 12

Chapter 5 Test

1. True
2. True
3. True
4. -224
5. -9
6. 22
7. A
8. C
9. C
10. C
11. E
12. B
13. E
14. A
15. No
16. Yes
17. 2
18. 1
19. 6
20. $-\frac{18}{5}$
21. $\frac{5}{19}$
22. $-\frac{1}{4}$
23. $\frac{11}{7}$
24. 3
25. 70 mph

Chapter 6 Test

1. True
2. True
3. False
4. $-\frac{2}{3}$
5. -22
6. -45
7. E
8. B
9. C
10. B
11. E
12. D
13. Yes
14. No
15. Yes
16. 8
17. 6
18. $\frac{9}{5}$
19. 13
20. $\frac{4}{7}$
21. Identity

22. -4
23. 2
24. False equation
25. 4 minutes

Chapter 7 Test

1. True
2. True
3. True
4. B
5. E
6. C
7. B
8. E
9. E
10. E
11. D
12. A
13. C
14. B
15. E
16. D
17. B
18. Yes
19. No
20. 15
21. $-\frac{34}{3}$
22. $-\frac{2}{5}$
23. 19
24. -1
25. 12 ounces

Chapter 8 Test

1. True
2. True
3. $\frac{9}{13}$
4. 1 : 5
5. A
6. C
7. D
8. B
9. E
10. A
11. E
12. D
13. C
14. $45y$
15. $21x$
16. D
17. Yes
18. Yes
19. 0.3
20. $\frac{1}{8}$
21. 1
22. $\frac{5}{12}$
23. -7
24. -4
25. 308 tennis balls

Chapter 9 Test

1. True
2. False
3. -8
4. 10
5. 1.14×10^{13}
6. 5.4×10^{-9}
7. 4.48×10^{10}
8. 5×10^{-6}
9. y^2 square inches
10. 11^3 or 1,331 cubic feet
11. C
12. E
13. A
14. D
15. E
16. C
17. E
18. B
19. C
20. A

21. D
22. $-\frac{2}{17}$
23. -5
24. $\frac{14}{5}$
25. 59 dimes

Chapter 10 Test

1. True
2. True
3. 2
4. 7
5. Irrational
6. Rational
7. $\sqrt{23}$
8. 9
9. 3.32
10. 6.56
11. 3
12. 32
13. C
14. E
15. D
16. C
17. E
18. B
19. No
20. Yes
21. $\frac{11}{3}$
22. 27
23. $-\frac{7}{9}$
24. 6
25. 9 years

Chapter 11 Test

1. True
2. True
3. B
4. C
5. E
6. A
7. 2.911×10^{11}
8. 3.5×10^{-8}
9. E
10. A
11. E
12. D
13. C
14. A
15. E
16. A
17. D
18. C
19. E
20. D
21. 0, -3
22. -12, -1
23. 0.45, -4.45
24. 0.12, -4.12
25. $7,500

Chapter 12 Test

1. True
2. True
3. 1.17×10^{17}
4. 5×10^{3}
5. E
6. E
7. Yes
8. Yes
9. $y=-9$
10. $y=-4$
11. No
12. Yes
13. -22
14. $\frac{2}{5}$
15. 4, -4
16. -2.35, -7.65
17. 0, -2
18. 5, -4

19.

y=4x-1

x	-2	-1	0	1	2	3
y	-9	-5	-1	3	7	11

20.

y=11-2x

x	-2	-1	0	1	2	3
y	15	13	11	9	7	5

21. 108.8 feet per second
22. 3.1 seconds
23. D
24. A
25. 79

Chapter 13 Test

1. True
2. True
3. A
4. E
5. B
6. D
7. A
8. C
9. B
10. E
11. D
12. A
13. Yes
14. No
15. 3
16. $-\frac{5}{3}$
17. 9, 0
18. 6, 2
19.

3y-2x=1

x	-2	-1	0	1	2	3
y	-1	$-\frac{1}{3}$	$\frac{1}{3}$	1	$\frac{5}{3}$	$\frac{7}{3}$

20.

z=3xy

x	-2	-1	0	1	2	3
y	3	4	5	6	7	8
z	-18	-12	0	18	42	72

21. $z = 8$
22. $A = -12$
23. D
24. E
25. 50 mph

Chapter 14 Test

1. True
2. True
3. True
4. and 5.

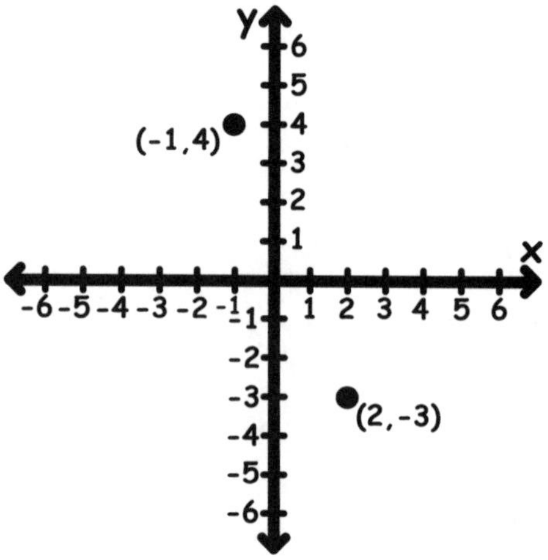

6. D
7. A
8. D
9. B
10. 4
11. -2
12. 4.58, -4.58
13. $y = 2$
14. $y = -4$
15. $z = -9$
16. A
17. C
18. E

19. A
20. x-intercept: $(-5,0)$; y-intercept: $(0,5)$
21. x-intercept: $(-3,0)$; y-intercept: $(0,6)$
22. E
23. B
24. 4 feet

Chapter 15 Test

1. True
2. False
3. D
4. B
5. C
6. A
7. Yes
8. Yes
9. -50
10. -7
11. $3.87, -3.87$
12. $z=32$
13. B
14. $-\frac{3}{2}$
15. 0
16. 2
17. $-\frac{3}{4}$
18. Slope: 3; y-intercept: $(0,-1)$
19. Slope: $-\frac{1}{4}$; y-intercept: $(0,5)$
20. Slope: $\frac{3}{2}$; y-intercept: $(0,4)$
21. C
22. E
23. D
24. A
25. 1,000 seconds

Chapter 16 Test

1. True
2. False
3. True
4. C
5. B
6. C
7. E
8. A
9. C
10. No
11. Yes
12. $0, -3$
13. $-2, -7$
14. $p=8$
15. B
16. Slope: 2; y-intercept: $(0,3)$
17. Slope: -10; y-intercept: $(0,0)$
18. D
19. A
20. $x=4,\ y=2$
21. $x=-3,\ y=-12$
22. C
23. E
24. a.) 29 adults
    b.) 16 children

Chapter 17 Test

1. False
2. True
3. C
4. D
5. A
6. $\sqrt{5}$
7. A
8. D
9. E
10. A
11. Slope = 15; y-intercept $=(0,2)$
12. Slope = $-\frac{1}{6}$; y-intercept $=(0,0)$
13. $x=3,\ y=6$
14. $x=-7,\ y=14$
15. B
16. E

17. B
18. C
19. E
20. A
21. E
22. D
23. C
24. 3 hours

Chapter 18 Test

1. True
2. True
3. 8
4. $\frac{11}{6}$
5. Function
6. Not a function
7. Function
8. Not a function
9. D
10. B
11. 18
12. −7
13. $x=2,\ y=-1$
14. $x=-2,\ y=3$
15. E
16. C
17. B
18. C
19. A
20. A
21. $x=5,\ x=-5$
22. $x=13,\ x=-3$
23. $x=-7$
24. C

Chapter 19 Test

1. True
2. True
3. $x=3$
4. $x=-\frac{5}{6}$
5. $x=\frac{22}{3}$
6. $x=9$
7. $x=4,\ x=-4$
8. $x=\frac{3}{8},\ x=-\frac{5}{8}$
9. B
10. A
11. Median = 19.45
12. Mean = 20.05; Range = 9.1
13. B
14. Median = 41.3; 28.7
15. Range = 65.7; Above the median
16. 18 children
17. 24 children
18. 4; Mode = 3.2
19. Median = 3.8; Range = 9.2
20. 0.375
21. $\frac{1}{6}$
22. $\frac{1}{64}$
23. 40%
24. $22,000